Joyfully Jewish

ב"ס"ד
Volume 2

# How to Awaken Your G‑dly Soul

## Rae Shagalov

A Creative Coloring Journal
of Calligraphy Artnotes &
Jewish Soul Adventures

Adapted from Lectures
By Rabbi Elchonon Tauber

Holy
Sparks

## Contact the author or publisher.
### E-mail: info • holysparks.com

- For wholesale discounts and bulk discounts for groups and teachers

- To arrange a creative workshop or author event with Rae Shagalov

- For custom calligraphy or Artnotes from classes, live or recorded

- To dedicate a volume in the Joyfully Jewish series
  in memory or honor of someone special

- For personal coaching to help elevate your Jewish connection,
  creativity, Life Purpose, or spiritual growth

Printed in the United States of America
First Printing, 2019


ISBN: 978-1-937472-02-3  paperback


# Holy Sparks Press
# WWW.HOLYSPARKS.COM


28 Sivan 5779
Los Angeles

Please do not color on Shabbat or Jewish holy days
as writing and coloring are prohibited by Jewish law on those days.

This is a gift for:

From:

May you be blessed
with success
and only good things

Holy Sparks

# ✑PRAISE FOR RAE SHAGALOV'S
# JOYFULLY JEWISH ARTNOTES ✒

"TAKE A CREATIVE JOURNEY INTO YOUR JEWISH SOUL! Rae's delightful illustrations and inspiring words take you step by step into pure connection, relaxation and visualized tranquility." -B. B. Romm-

"FULL OF COOL THINGS TO COLOR! It's not only full of cool things to color.....each page is a whole 'lesson' for a JOYFUL JEWISH LIFE!!! I can't wait to give them to friends, family, and of course, to get coloring!!!!" –Malka F.-

"I FEEL CALMER AND HAPPIER! Rae's Artnotes make me feel calmer and help me correct my negative thoughts. I love how her art brings me into my center and helps me to remember what is important and what is not – and that my priority needs to be to serve Hashem b'simcha, with joy, no matter what!" -Shoshanna P.-

"BEAUTIFUL AND DEEP! I was inspired by the beautiful art and deep, important, and Chassidic topics Rae chose to write about, clearly written with love and a deep caring for a fellow Jew." – Elisheva K., Chabad House, Washington Heights, NYC-

"STUDY AND UNDERSTAND TORAH! Although I'm not Jewish, Rae's artwork and quotes have deepened my desire to study and understand Torah and the G-d of Abraham, Isaac, and Jacob. Rae's joyful attitude toward G-d is compelling and inviting." -Tracy T, Kansas-

"SPIRITUALLY UPLIFTING! This is the most spiritually uplifting experience a family or individual can do! Opportunity to be creative and also touch that still small voice we often miss in this noisy world!" –W.S.-

"THE CALLIGRAPHY IS MAGNIFICENT! What a beautiful book. The writings are so very inspirational and the calligraphy is magnificent." –Phaedra-

LITTLE BOOSTS OF LIGHT! "I surround myself with Rae's art in my home office. I love that whenever I get overwhelmed or discouraged, I can just look up and the Holy Sparks Artnotes are like little boosts of light that help me turn my dark thoughts into positive action." -Esther Ginsburg, Producer of "Lights and Miracle Days"-

"BEAUTIFUL, UPLIFTING WISDOM! Such beautiful, uplifting wisdom in such a short amount of words! I keep buying more of these to give out to my friends."- A.N.-

11 Iyar 5774
May 11, 2014

We have known Rae Shagalov of Holy Sparks over 15 years. During these years she has been a frequent visitor at our home. Rae has a unique talent and ability. While she is listening to shiurim she will often transcribe the key words of inspiration and lessons into truly beautiful works of art.

She has come to many of the *shiurim* (lectures) I have given over the years in various venues and faithfully writes down the key points. I have reviewed her notes of some of the *shiurim* which she has transcribed and I hereby verify the accuracy of what she has quoted from my teachings and authorize the publication of these notes.

It is my sincere hope and wish that you, dear reader, will absorb some of these teachings and apply them to your personal life and hopefully gain some insight and broader knowledge of our Holy Torah's teachings and specifically the teachings of Reb Nachman of Breslov OB"M, whose words of wisdom I often quote.

I can personally attest to the benefits of internalizing some of these lessons which have made a huge impact on my life and the lives of my family. It is common knowledge that the practice of meditation and taking the time to think about our lives and how much Hashem has blessed us with, can truly effect great changes.

As I have often said, we live with far more conveniences than Shlomo Hamelech did so many years ago. Yet, how often do we take the time to truly appreciate the modern day conveniences with which we live and take so much for granted?

It is my fervent wish that these words of enlightenment bring many blessings into your lives and the lives of your loved ones. My best wishes to Rae for much success in this undertaking.

Rabbi Elchonon Tauber

# ❧ CLAIM YOUR FREE BONUS! ❧

Be sure to sign up for your gifts at:

## WWW.JOYFULLYJEWISH.COM/PROJECT/FREEBIES

Not one... Not two... But THREE Free Printable Downloads for you to choose from (you can have all 3 if you like!). Choose the self-care checklist & mini-retreat, the women's mitzvahs creativity pack, or the Jewish Meditation Soul Adventure.

Feel free to share this link with your friends!

# ❧ MY DEEP APPRECIATION & GRATITUDE ❧

I am deeply grateful to Rabbi Elchonon and Rebbetzin Hendy Tauber
for allowing me to publish my Artnotes from Rabbi Tauber's classes,
to Rebbetzin Sterna Citron and Terri Levin for editing this work so carefully,
and to my dear husband, Rabbi Yosef Yitzchok for his help with *everything!*

## LET'S CONNECT!
Facebook.com/soultips
Pinterest.com/holysparks
Twitter.com/holysparks
Youtube.com/holysparksbooks
Instagram.com/holysparks

I would love to hear your insights and questions, and see your colorful creations, so let's connect! Feel free to email me with questions, suggestions & pictures of your coloring at: HELLO@JOYFULLYJEWISH.COM

SIGN UP TO RECEIVE FREE ART, COLORING PAGES
& RAE SHAGALOV'S JOYFULLY JEWISH ARTNOTES NEWSLETTER!
Go to: WWW.JOYFULLYJEWISH.COM

This Publication Is Dedicated To The Rebbe,
Rabbi Menachem M. Schneerson of Lubavitch

whose teachings and inspiration lives in us, and fires us up
to try and reach heights we can't reach on our own,
to prepare the whole world for the imminent arrival of Moshiach.

IN LOVING MEMORY OF

Harav Schneur Zalman Halevi ע"ה
ben Harav Yitzchok Elchonon Halevi הי"ד Shagalov

Reb Dovid Asniel ben Reb Eliyahu ע"ה

Devora Rivka bas Reb Yosef Eliezer ע"ה

Reb Yitzchok Moshe ben Reb Dovid Asniel ע"ה

᪥   May Their Souls Merit Eternal Life   ᪣

AND IN HONOR OF

Mrs. Esther Shaindel bas Fraidel Chedva שתחי' Shagalov
and Our Dear Children and Grandchildren שיחיו
May You Always Be Joyfully Jewish!

DEDICATED BY

Rabbi & Mrs. Yosef Yitzchok and Gittel Rachel שיחיו Shagalov

To dedicate future editions in
honor or memory of your
loved ones, contact us at:
info@holysparks.com

# ❧ INTRODUCTION TO THE *JOYFULLY JEWISH* SERIES ☙

I love being Jewish! But I didn't always. In fact, I left Judaism for 10 years and became a "spiritual tourist." You see, when I was growing up, I never learned about the spiritual secrets of authentic Torah. I thought there was no such thing as Jewish meditation or Jewish spirituality. I didn't even think Jews were supposed to be happy! Then, through developing my craft as a calligrapher, I discovered the mystical secrets of Judaism. When I began to explore the alef bet, letter-by-letter, the holy Hebrew letters led me on a quest to discover a deep, soulful, joyful Judaism I never knew existed.

By the grace of G-d, from the very beginning of my Torah learning I discovered my talent as a Jewish artist. I realized that what I was learning was so profound, I wanted to be sure to review my notes over and over again and to share these Torah secrets with others. I began to write my notes in calligraphy. I had classical training and was already a professional calligrapher, and I began to "doodle". I knew that people would enjoy coloring in my doodles as they read and absorbed the Jewish wisdom on each page.

One of my earliest teachers in Los Angeles was Rabbi Elchonon Tauber. Rabbi Tauber has a gift for bringing down the loftiest concepts to the simplest understanding so that anyone at any level of Torah learning can benefit. Most of his classes that I attended were based on the teachings of Rabbi Nachman of Breslov [1772-1810]. Rabbi Tauber very generously shares his broad Torah knowledge and sweet smile of love for every Jew to encourage each of us to do our best, smile often, be happy, and talk to G-d every day of our lives. With G-d's help, I wrote the Artnotes in this volume of the *Joyfully Jewish* series in Rabbi Tauber's classes between 1999-2016.

I love to learn the secrets of Torah, about the intricacies of our soul, and how the universe is designed to help us transform this world into a dwelling place for G-d. With the help of G-d, over the last 25 years, I've gone to thousands of classes and written more than 3,000 pages of calligraphy Artnotes that capture the essence of each class. This Jewish wisdom from hundreds of our greatest Torah leaders gives us a very important message for our special time at the threshold of the Messianic Era* of peace. I call these Artnotes the "field notes of the last generation of exile and the first generation of Geula.**

It really bothers me that so many Jewish people (like me when I was growing up) have no clue about the treasures of their own amazing spiritual inheritance. It is urgent that we each do everything we can to understand how to prepare ourselves and the world for the great time of peace and abundance we have all been waiting for. In this time of violence and suffering and economic uncertainty, we each MUST do our utmost to bring Moshiach* NOW!

---

*Moshiach & the Messianic Era: Moshiach is the Jewish messiah, the long-awaited Redeemer who will bring us out of the exile of this world into an amazing world filled with the revelation of G-dliness in every aspect of Creation. The word *Moshiach* in Hebrew means "anointed". One of the principles of Jewish faith according to Maimonides is that one day there will arise a dynamic Jewish leader, a direct descendant of the Davidic dynasty, who will rebuild the Temple in Jerusalem and gather Jews from all over the world and bring them back to the Land of Israel. In every generation, Moshiach is ready to be revealed when we have finished preparing the world to receive him. Every man, woman and child has an individual responsibility and priviledge to work to bring about Moshiach's coming, using his or her unique talents and situation.

**The Lubavitcher Rebbe, Rabbi Menachem Mendel Schneerson, taught us that we must -- now -- "live with the Redemption," experience a foretaste of it and anticipate it in our daily conduct. This means living our lives in a way that parallels the way we would live in the time of the Redemption.

The *Joyfully Jewish* series began with the *Joyfully Jewish Family and Adult Coloring Book* that integrates the relaxing, meditative art of coloring with deep Chassidic secrets of Judaism. It includes fun designs to color, unique Jewish quotes from contemporary Jewish masters written in beautiful calligraphy, and is an uplifting introduction to Jewish spirituality. The graphic images from that coloring book came from my Artnotes sketchbooks.

The *Joyfully Jewish* series of Artnotes includes many full-page and smaller images to color, but unlike the coloring book, it is much richer and fuller in calligraphy text and field notes from the Jewish wisdom classes in which they were drawn. Most of the pages are copies of the original Artnotes pages, just as I wrote and drew them during the classes.

The first volume of the series is "*Create Your Joyfully Jewish Life!*" (available on Amazon.com). It's a six-week creative journaling workbook, filled with calligraphy Artnotes, Soul Adventures, & coloring pages to guide you, step-by-step, to create a happy, healthy, and meaningul Jewish life.

My goal for the Joyfully Jewish series is to provide you with a pleasant, fun, and interactive, journey into Jewish learning. It's very important for you to engage with what you're learning so that you can really integrate it into your life in a joyful way. There are many areas for you to color and blank pages for you to record your thoughts, insights, good resolutions, doodles and dreams for your life and the Messianic Era soon to come, please G-d.

I've also included *Soul Adventures* to help you integrate the profound Jewish wisdom you'll be learning in this book. What is a Soul Adventure? A Soul Adventure is a journey above time and space to explore the vast, fascinating chambers of your own soul and the G-dly hints, echoes, whispers, and holy sparks that are hidden in your innermost self. Soul Adventures are creative exercises that help you look deeply at your life and make significant, transformative changes to improve it. Some of the Soul Adventures in this book were developed in *Joyfully Jewish* workshops that I have led. You can find more information about these workshops and author book tours at the back of this book.

I would love to see your colorful creations, so let's connect! Feel free to email me with questions, suggestions, personal insights, or reflections you'd like to share - and, of course, pictures of your coloring. Please share them with me via email at: INFO@HOLYSPARKS.COM or on any of my social media channels listed at the front of this book.

It is with great humility that I offer to you the second volume of Artnotes in my *Joyfully Jewish* series. It is my great hope that they will inspire you, deepen your love of Torah, increase your motivation to do mitzvahs, and help you feel closer to G-d in every moment of your life.

May G-d keep you from all manner of harm and distress and bless the works of your hands with success, in good health, with great joy and abundant livelihood, and may you always be *Joyfully Jewish!*

*May you be blessed with success and only good things!*

**Rae Shagalov**

Holy Sparks

# ❧ HOW TO USE THIS BOOK ❧

## SURROUND YOURSELF WITH INSPIRATION, ART & FRIENDS

Invite your family and friends to join you in the fun. Feel free to take this book apart and share the pages or have some extra copies of the book on hand to share or give as gifts. Hang up the Artnotes that inspire you the most, just as they are, or colored in by you, your family and your friends. Surround yourself with this love and inspiration to keep you moving forward and higher in your life and work.

This book is not intended to be read from beginning to end in one sitting. The pages do not need to be read in order. You can skip around to what attracts you the most, read from beginning to end, or open to a random page. You can simply enjoy the calligraphy Artnotes and let the deep Jewish wisdom seep into your soul and inspire you, or you can interact with the wisdom playfully by coloring in the images, writing and doodling on the journal pages, and engaging in the Soul Adventures.

## CREATE A JOURNAL IN THE BOOK

There are journal pages in the book for you to record any insights and challenges that arise when you read through the Artnotes. You can also use these journal pages to doodle or write poetry, imagine or envision what you hope your life can be, or to use creatively in any way you choose. Explore your inner world through the prompts provided in each Soul Adventure. Sketch and twirl your pen in between writing your thoughts or if you feel stuck and unable to write. These doodles will relax and focus you and may provide a wealth of understanding of the subconscious and sublime whispers of your soul.

## COLOR IT IN!

Coloring is a very relaxing, peaceful, meditative activity. As you color in the pages, contemplate the Artnotes thoughts on them and try to internalize them. If you're doing this as a family activity, discuss the ideas while you color them in together. Afterwards, hang up these beautiful family treasures around your home to set a Joyfully Jewish tone.

Coloring can help you relax into a peaceful and contemplative mood, so for best results, turn off the phone, computer and any other stressful distractions, if you can. Place a piece of cardboard or a few sheets of paper underneath the page if you are using pens so the ink won't bleed through.

Gather your colored pencils or pens. Flip through the book and choose a page that sparks your interest. Intuitively choose your colors and don't fret if you make a "mistake" or color outside the lines. Just relax and continue, letting your mind wander and enjoy the colors. Being in this relaxed state will improve your life and outlook, but you can also use it to go higher into holiness. How do you do this?

You could listen to a Torah class while coloring, or you could meditate on the greatness of G-d. When you are in this relaxed state, it is a very good time to think about and speak to G-d. It's a wonderful place to be in to think about your life, your family and friends and how you can improve yourself and your relationships. It's a lovely interlude for creatively thinking about a new mitzvah you would like to do, or imagining how you could do a mitzvah more beautifully than before. It's a special time to dream about what the world will be like when Moshiach comes, G-d willing, very, very soon to usher in the great era of peace that we all wait and wish for. When you do this, you elevate the act of coloring by serving G-d with it.

# ❦ CONTENTS ❧

INTRODUCTION                                         8
A NOTE ABOUT G-D                                    13

PAIN, DIFFICULTIES & CHALLENGES                     15

PEACE                                               51

LOVE                                                69

GOODNESS                                            89

HAPPINESS                                          113

GLOSSARY                                           148

ABOUT HOLYSPARKS,
RABBI TAUBER, & THE AUTHOR                         150

10 WAYS TO BE JOYFULLY JEWISH                      152

7 SPECIAL MITZVAHS FOR
RIGHTEOUS GENTILES                                 154

BOOKS & ONLINE COURSES
BY RAE SHAGALOV                                     156

A FREE BONUS FOR YOU                               158

WORKSHOPS, COACHING
& COMMISSIONS                                       159

These Hebrew letters appear at the top of each Artnotes page:

בס"ד

This is an abbreviation for the Aramaic phrase "B'Sayata Di'Shmaya,"
which means, "With the Help of Heaven."

OR

בי"ה

This is an abbreviation for Baruch Hashem (Blessed is the Name of G-d
or B'ezrat Hashem (With the help of G-d)

Putting these letters at the top of every page reminds us that everything
comes from G-d and that we need His help in everything we do.

# ❧A NOTE ABOUT G-D*❧

## WHY SHOULD YOU TALK TO HASHEM?**

There are many benefits to talking to G-d. You will feel calmer and happier when you know that you are never truly alone. You will increase your faith, improve your character, and have more energy to meet your challenges when you are connected to G-d's infinite source of strength. *Hitbodedut* (meditation) cleanses your soul, connects you to holiness, and improves all of your relationships with other people, with yourself, and with G-d.

For best results and a deeper relationship, make an appointment with Hashem every day. Dedicate a set amount of time each day, and don't let anything stop you! Start with just one minute, if you have to, and just show up – even if you don't feel like it or you have nothing to say. By the end of 30 days, you will wonder how you ever lived without talking to G-d every day.

## WHY IS G-D REFERRED TO AS "HE"?

Isn't G-d infinitely beyond any gender? Yes, G-d is beyond gender, but we're not. Through the Torah, *Chassidut*, and the mystical *Kabbalah*, we learn the secrets of how G-d created the universe. When the kabbalists describe the exquisite dance and love relationship between the transcendental and the imminent presence of G-d in this world, the transcendent aspect of the infinite Holy One is presented in the masculine. The immanent divine presence or *Shechinah* and we, who reach for the relationship, are described in the feminine.

*To protect G-d's name, we don't spell it out completely. The Jewish people do not write G-d's name in a place where it may be discarded, erased, or carried into an unclean place. Please note that this book should not be taken into a bathroom.

**We often use the Hebrew word "Hashem," which means "The Name," instead of using G-d's name. Treating G-d's name with this extra reverence is a way to protect the holiness and sanctity of G-d's name.

To learn more about Jewish meditation and get inspired to start a daily practice, you may order Rae Shagalov's beautifully illustrated book, *"The Secret Art of Talking to G-d,"* on Amazon at: http://bit.ly/talking-to-G-d

בס"ד

Pain,
Difficulties,
& Challenges

# ✿ SOUL ADVENTURE #1 ✿

MAKE A LIST of the challenges in your life.
CHOOSE one challenge that you would like to change.
IMAGINE: What do you feel is G-d's wish for you in this challenge?
CHANGE: What is one small change you could make in the situation
or in your attitude toward it that you could begin today to be happier?

## WRITE OR DOODLE YOUR ANSWERS BELOW.
If you need more room, continue on the following journal pages.

בס"ד

Hurray! Another day of challenges! Another day to live!

Grab the gift of life into your hands!

It takes time and effort to change, but you can do it. Really! Just change one thing.

Holy Sparks

WWW.HOLYSPARKS.COM
©1990-2016 Rae Shagalov
16.68

# ❧ SOUL ADVENTURE #2 ❧

Try to track the number of times you kvetch for 5 days.
See if you can decrease the number by 50%.

## KVETCH TRACKER

| MON. | TUE. | WED. | THU. | FRI. |
|------|------|------|------|------|
|      |      |      |      |      |
|      |      |      |      |      |
|      |      |      |      |      |
|      |      |      |      |      |
|      |      |      |      |      |
|      |      |      |      |      |
|      |      |      |      |      |
|      |      |      |      |      |
|      |      |      |      |      |
|      |      |      |      |      |

# ❧ YOUR NOTES, INSIGHTS, DAYDREAMS & DOODLES ❧

בס"ד

Everyone has a kvetch inside.
The more responsible you are, the less you'll kvetch.

THE DAY YOU COMPLIMENT YOUR SPOUSE MORE THAN YOU CRITICISE IS THE DAY YOU'LL HAVE A GREAT MARRIAGE.

**We're born to kvetch.** CRITICISM COMES EASY. IT FLOWS. TO BE POSITIVE TAKES MORE EFFORT, BUT IT'S WORTH IT.

In the darkest of darkness you can find the biggest light, The Light of G‑d.

When you go through your personal darkness, this is G‑d's call to you, "Come and find Me." This is *your* challenge.

When you are happy, it's easier to do the right thing. When you have to do something hard, start with JOY.

When you do Holy things 100%, you feel 100% better.

Make your day a real day.

THE SUN WILL RISE AND SET WITH OR WITHOUT YOUR SMILE, SO WHY NOT JUST BE HAPPY?

Try to be really HAPPY! SMILING IS CONTAGIOUS. SPREAD YOUR SMILE AROUND THE WHOLE WORLD.

Take charge of your day and make it a happy one.

5770   23.45   "Malkhus"   47TH DAY OF THE OMER HOD SHEB'MALKHUS   Holy Sparks

בס"ד

There is nothing
outside of G‑d.

This is
our big
mistake
in life:
WE THINK LIFE
IS SUPPOSED
TO BE EASY,
SMOOTH,
WITHOUT ANY
PROBLEMS.

HOW CAN WE
STRENGTHEN OUR
FAITH WHEN THINGS
HAPPEN?

By
saying:
"G‑d
runs
The
world,"
WHENEVER YOU
EXPERIENCE
ANYTHING GOOD
OR ANYTHING
THAT DOESN'T
LOOK GOOD.

THERE IS
NOTHING
OUTSIDE
OF G‑D.

Behold!
I am with you.
You are not
alone.

G‑d is with you
every single second.
When challenging things
happen, say,

"G‑d is with me.
For some reason that I do
not yet understand, G‑d
wants this for my ultimate
good."

Your challenges are
custom-made for you
to bring out your
inner strength,
and maximize your growth.

Holy
Sparks

Rabbi Elchonon Tauber MAAYON YISROEL LOS ANGELES
LIKUTEY MOHARAN 155                                    22.66

WWW.HOLYSPARKS.COM
©1990-2016 Rae Shagalov

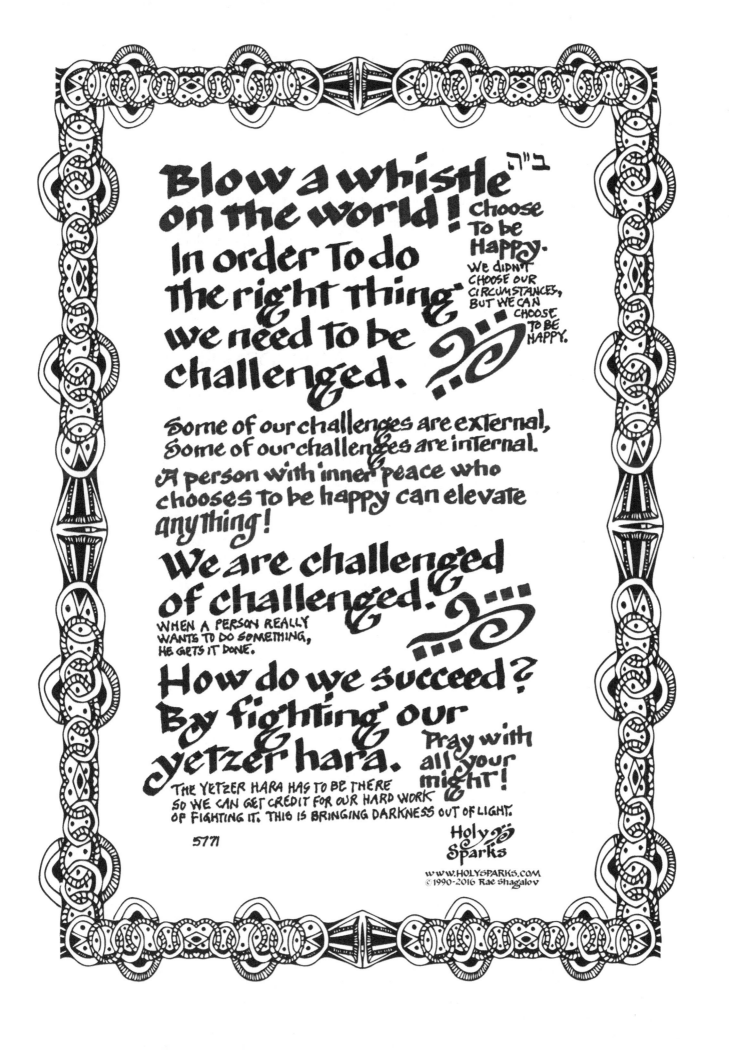

Blow a whistle on the world! בס"ד

In order to do the right thing we need to be challenged.

Choose to be Happy.
We didn't choose our circumstances, but we can choose to be happy.

Some of our challenges are external, some of our challenges are internal.

A person with inner peace who chooses to be happy can elevate anything!

We are challenged of challenged.

When a person really wants to do something, he gets it done.

How do we succeed? By fighting our yetzer hara.

Pray with all your might!

The yetzer hara has to be there so we can get credit for our hard work of fighting it. This is bringing darkness out of light.

5771

Holy Sparks

# ❧ SOUL ADVENTURE #3 ❧

## MEDITATION

LIMIT: Set a timer for 10 or 20 minutes.

SECLUDE: In a quiet place (a field, forest, beach, or private room), talk to G-d about your problems.

CHOOSE one problem. Tell the problem how big G-d is.

IMAGINE: Have an imaginary conversation with the problem about different ways that G-d, the Almighty Master of the Universe, might transform the problem into revealed good in your life.

Be wild and crazy with your ideas – G-d has no limits and wants only what's good for you!

## WRITE OR DOODLE YOUR IDEAS BELOW.
If you need more room, continue on the following journal pages.

# YOUR NOTES, INSIGHTS, & DOODLES

בס"ד

# In your pain and in your joy...

HOW TO HAVE A GREAT MARRIAGE: COMPLIMENT AT LEAST AS OFTEN AS YOU CRITICIZE - AND WITH AS MUCH PASSION.

**Your life is a gift given to you by G‑d!**

400 IS THE POWER OF IMPURITY.

הַנֵּה

→ MALKHUS: THE KINGDOM OF G‑D

THE NUN FELL. WE ALL HAVE A REBELLIOUSNESS WITHIN US.

WE HAVE TO LIFT THE NUN WHERE IT FALLS. HOW?

**By remembering there is a G‑d in the world.**

CYCLES OF 28

## By thanking G‑d,
YOU FEEL G‑D'S PRESENCE IN YOUR LIFE. FOCUS ON THE GOODNESS IN YOUR LIFE.

IF YOU DON'T APPRECIATE WHAT YOU HAVE, THEN YOU DON'T HAVE WHAT YOU HAVE!

## Leah never stopped praying,
AND SHE WAS BLESSED TO BEAR SIX OF THE TRIBES.

# Never give up your dreams!
DON'T LOSE YOUR FOCUS!

# Rabbi Elchonon Tauber
PARSHAS VAYISHLACH BRESLOV SHUL @

Do you run away from yourself? WE ALL SAY, "I DON'T HAVE ENOUGH TIME FOR MYSELF! I DON'T HAVE TIME TO SIT AND TALK TO G‑D!" THE TRUTH IS, WE ALL HAVE TIME. BUT WE RUN AWAY FROM OURSELVES...BY DOING, DOING, DOING.

# You can find G‑d in every situation.
## You are never alone in this world.

Yes, you are going to have a lot of pain and difficulties. You do not know what tomorrow is going to bring. If you bring G‑d into your life every day, you will feel a special sweetness in your life.

BRING G‑D INTO YOURSELF, INTO YOUR PAIN.

Holy Sparks

WWW.HOLYSPARKS.COM
©1990-2016 Rae Shagalov

IF YOU DON'T GIVE UP, G‑D WILL HELP YOU.

DID YOUR DAY GO ANY BETTER TODAY BECAUSE YOU REFUSED TO SMILE? NO MATTER WHAT HAPPENS, SMILING WILL IMPROVE YOUR SITUATION.

EVEN IF YOU CAN'T OPEN YOUR MOUTH, SIT FOR 20 MINUTES AND TRY TO TALK TO G‑D.

15.1

# ❧ SOUL ADVENTURE #4 ❧
## MEDITATION

Whenever you experience a challenging or frustrating situation today say:
*"G-d loves me. G-d REALLY loves me."*

# ❧ YOUR NOTES, INSIGHTS, & DOODLES ❧

If you knew
how much
G‑d loves you,
you would always
feel secure.
Walk around a whole day thinking:
G‑d ...And watch
loves The miracles
me. appear in your
G‑d really life!
loves me.

בס"ד

Holy Sparks
www.HOLYSPARKS.COM
© 1990-2016 Rae Shagalov

# ❧ SOUL ADVENTURE #5 ❧

LIST: Make a list of all of the important people in your life.
WRITE: Next to each person, write the qualities you appreciate or any good points about them.
CHOOSE one or more person.
WRITE a note or tell them what you appreciate about them.
REFLECT: What was the response of the person that you appreciated?

בס"ד

You have no idea how precious are your efforts in the eyes of G‑d.

The more good you look for, the more good you'll find, …

IN YOUR SPOUSE
IN YOUR CHILDREN
IN YOUR BOSS
IN YOUR LIFE
IN YOUR PARENTS
IN YOUR SIBLINGS
IN YOUR SITUATION

G‑d is not out to get you. G‑d is not punishing you.

The hardships you go through cleanse you, purify you, and bring out strengths you didn't know you had.

RABBI ELCHONON TAUBER
AT MAAYAN YISROEL
V' Kislev 5770

Holy Sparks

22.69

# ✎ SOUL ADVENTURE #6 ✎

LIST every good thing you can remember about your day today or yesterday.

בס"ד

From
Every pain
we suffer
good comes out.

In the bleakest
moment, there
is what to
sing about.

On a bad day,
see what
goodness you
can find.

Holy
Sparks
WWW.HOLYSPARKS.COM
©1990-2016 Rae Shagalov

# YOUR NOTES, INSIGHTS, & DOODLES

# Let your inner pain come out and explode to G‑d.

EVERY DAY YOU HAVE A STANDING APPOINTMENT WITH AN INCREDIBLE LISTENER...

IMAGINE YOU HAVE A SPECIAL TIME ALONE EVERY DAY WITH THE PRESIDENT TO SAY WHATEVER YOU WANT TO SAY. NOW IMAGINE THAT YOU HAVE A SPECIAL TIME ALONE EVERY DAY WITH THE CREATOR OF THE UNIVERSE. YOU REALLY DO! TALK TO G‑D TODAY!

If you remember your days are numbered, then every day counts.

WHY DO PEOPLE FIGHT? TO WASTE TIME; TO AVOID DOING WHAT WE WERE CREATED TO DO.

Every day, remind yourself: Another day like this might never come again!

YOU HAVE TO DEVELOP A LOVE FOR WHAT YOU DO.

# Every person has an angel who helps him or her through life.

## This is what G‑d wanted.

EVERY PERSON HAS HARDSHIPS. THE QUESTION IS: HOW WILL YOU REACT TO YOUR DIFFICULTIES?

There is a part of us that wants to be unhappy, that wants to worry.

YOU WILL ALWAYS BE ABLE TO FIND SOMETHING TO PUT YOUR WORRY INTO. WHY BOTHER?

Just be happy.

Red = JUDGEMENT
White = MERCY
A PERSON NEEDS BOTH OF THESE POWERS IN THE HEART.

Deep respect and love = PEACE

Jews give up an incredible amount to be Jewish.

THE GREATNESS OF YEHUDAH WAS THAT HE ADMITTED HIS SHORTCOMINGS.

Every day, thank G‑d!

Holy Sparks

Rabbi Elchonon Tauber  15 Tevet 5752  WWW.HOLYSPARKS.COM ©1990-2016 Rae Shagalov

15.35

# ❧ YOUR NOTES, INSIGHTS, & DOODLES ❧

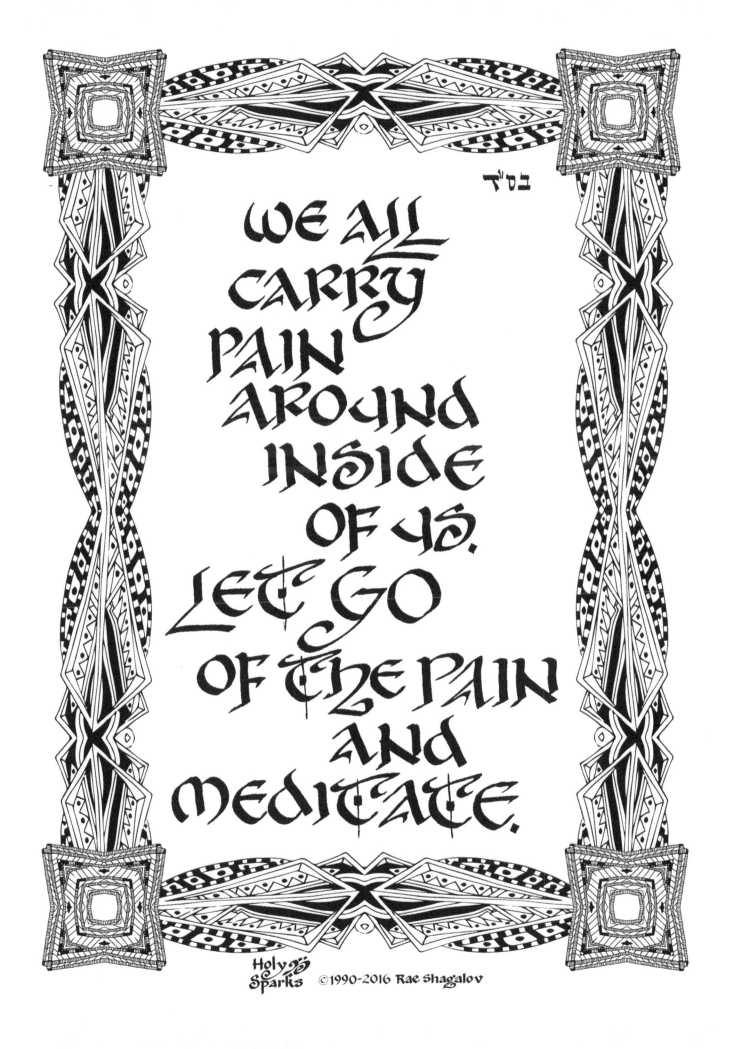

WE ALL CARRY PAIN AROUND INSIDE OF US. LET GO OF THE PAIN AND MEDITATE.

בס"ד

Holy Sparks ©1990-2016 Rae Shagalov

# ❧ SOUL ADVENTURE #7 ❧

LIST: What are your weaknesses that you would like to overcome?
REFLECT: Next to each weakness, write one small thing you could do to begin to strengthen or overcome it.

# RIBBONO SHEL OLAM... LISTEN TO MY PAIN

ב"ה

GⓈD IS UNBELIEVABLE! HE KNOWS ALL THE STARS BY NAME! DO YOU THINK HE FORGOT ABOUT YOU?! GⓈD LOVES YOU BETTER THAN ANYONE!

HE IS EVERYWHERE! HE LISTENS TO EVERYONE ALL AT THE SAME TIME! KVETCH TO HIM! CRY TO HIM! BEG HIM!

## FACE TO FACE

### INTIMACY

WHEN YOU LOOK SOMEONE IN THE FACE, WHEN YOU LOOK SOMEONE IN THE EYES, IT BRINGS YOU CLOSER.

THE KOHANIM WERE REQUIRED TO CARRY THE TABERNACLE TWO-BY-TWO, FACE-TO-FACE, AND THE MIRACLE WAS THAT THE TABERNACLE CARRIED THEM.

## THE STRENGTH OF A PERSON IS HIS WEAKNESS.

A KING ONCE HIRED A PAINTER TO MAKE A PORTRAIT OF MOSHE RABBEINU. THE KING HAD A READER OF FACES TELL HIM THE CHARACTER OF MOSHE RABBEINU FROM THE PORTRAIT. THIS EXPERT ON FACES TOLD EVERY CHARACTER TRAIT THAT MOSHE RABBEINU DID NOT HAVE, BECAUSE MOSHE RABBEINU WORKED HARD TO OVERCOME EVERY NEGATIVE TRAIT.

## THE WEAKNESS GIVES A PERSON THE DESIRE TO OVERCOME THAT WEAKNESS AND PURSUE PEACE

THE KOHANIM HAD A TENDENCY TOWARD ANGER, BUT THIS AROUSED IN THEM THE DESIRE TO OVERCOME THIS TENDENCY AND TO BE EVEN MORE PEACEFUL PEOPLE.

## EVERY GENERATION HAS ITS TEST

THE TEST OF OUR GENERATION IS TO OVERCOME LUST AND VIOLENCE AND TO BE MODEST, MORAL PEOPLE.

## Am I doing the right thing? Is there anything I can change?

WHAT STAYS WITH YOU FOREVER? THE KIND WORD YOU SAY TO SOMEONE, THE VISIT YOU MADE TO A SICK PERSON, THE CALL YOU MADE TO A DEPRESSED FRIEND.

## Money and People never stay together

BUT THE MITZVAHS YOU DO STAY WITH YOU FOREVER.

## Every piece of Judaism is so beautiful!

Holy Sparks

Rabbi Tauber Ahavas Yisroel Synagogue 74 5758

WWW.HOLYSPARKS.COM
©1990-2016 Rae Shagalov

# ❧ SOUL ADVENTURE #8 ❧

## REFLECTION:

1. What is one thing you want to change between you and G-d?

2. What is one thing you want to change between you and another person?

3. What is one thing you want to change between you and yourself?

בס"ד

# THE 1-MALKUS THAT FALLS.

### HASHEM holds up the ones that FALL.

when you fall,
Don't give up 🌿
🌿 GET UP!

Everyone has falls.
Everyone has ups & downs.
In that place that you fall,
Hashem is right there READY TO HELP YOU UP!

Accept consolation and move on ◎❖

## NEVER EVER GIVE UP.

No matter how many
times you have tried
and failed 🌿

## BEGIN ANEW NOW.

Choose two things to change:
One between you & HASHEM,
One between you & a person.
MEDITATE & ASK HASHEM
to help you change. BE BRAVE.

## DO NOT ❖ BE ❖ AFRAID.

PLEASE HASHEM
help me to overcome ...

HAPPINESS GIVES YOU
THE POWER TO BE BRAVE.

Holy 🌿 Sparks

Tu B'Av 5757 449

# SOUL ADVENTURE #9

## REFLECTION:

What do you think G-d wants from you right now, in this moment?

ב"ה

It's the way you look at things...
If you imagine that you just received a million dollars, almost everything is easy and sweet.

If you are not in a million dollar mood — Fake it!

Ask yourself what G‑d wants from you right now, in this moment.

Become an expert on your ups and downs.

Self-awareness comes through meditation. The best way to do meditation and Teshuva is to

Talk to G‑d.

Find G‑d in your ups and in your downs.

USE YOUR LOWS TO PROPEL YOURSELF BACK UP TO G‑D.

Teshuvah

If you don't keep rising and growing, you fall back.

G‑d is waiting for you to say Hello.

Take some time every day to talk to G‑d.

G‑d's love for YOU is infinite!

No matter how low you have sunk, no matter how far you have fallen, you can always bounce back to G‑d.

In my ups and in my downs I can always find Hashem.

THERE IS A PART OF US THAT WANTS TO RUN AWAY FROM G‑D. WHERE CAN WE GO? THERE IS NO PLACE WHERE G‑D IS NOT.

Holy Sparks
WWW.HOLYSPARKS.COM
© 1990-2016 Rae Shagalov

Elul 5770

23.91

# YOUR NOTES, INSIGHTS, & DOODLES

בס"ד

NEVER GIVE UP! No matter how many times you have tried and failed, BEGIN ANEW

NOW. NOW. NOW. NOW.

# ❧ SOUL ADVENTURE #10 ❧

## MEDITATION:

In your meditation today, look for the part of you that does not want peace.
Ask it what is the message it is trying to tell you about how you can grow and rise above it.

## ❧ YOUR NOTES, INSIGHTS, & DOODLES ❧

When things go well, Nobody ever asks: "Why me?"

Only when things go wrong do we ask, "Why me?"

WHERE IS G‑D? WHEREVER YOU LET HIM IN.

HOW DO YOU LET G‑D IN? TALK TO HASHEM. LET HIM INTO YOUR HEART. LET YOUR HEART OUT TO HASHEM. **100%**

THE SCIENTISTS SAY IT WOULD TAKE 17,000 YEARS JUST TO COUNT THE STARS IN THE MILKY WAY ALONE, AND YET HAKADOSH BORUCHU KNOWS ALL OF THE STARS BY NAME.

BEHOLD, I AM WITH YOU. I'LL WATCH OVER YOU WHEREVER YOU ARE.

LOVE yourself WITH LIFE

Holy Sparks
WWW.HOLYSPARKS.COM
©1990-2016 Rae Shagalov

THE LOVE OF HASHEM GOES WITH EVERY MITZVAH. YOU CANNOT LOVE SOMETHING IF YOU HAVE NO RELATIONSHIP WITH IT. THE MITZVAHS CREATE OUR RELATIONSHIP WITH HASHEM.

SEE FOR YOURSELF: KEEP A MEDITATION JOURNAL & RECORD HOW YOUR LIFE CHANGES.

IN EVERY MITZVAH IS THE LOVE OF HASHEM.

THERE IS A PART IN ALL OF US THAT DOES NOT WANT PEACE. THE CLOSER YOU COME TO HASHEM, THE MORE YOU CLEAVE TO HOLINESS, THE MORE YOU UNIFY WITH PEACE, EVEN TO THAT PART THAT DOES NOT WANT PEACE.

MEDITATE WITH WHAT YOU HAVE, WITH ALL YOUR SHORTCOMINGS. THE MORE YOU TALK TO HASHEM, THE MORE YOU ACCEPT WHO YOU ARE & THE MORE PEACEFUL YOU BECOME. YOU CAN'T FAKE A CRY WHEN YOU'RE ALONE WITH HASHEM.

In every situation, no matter how difficult, you can find Hashem, because especially in the difficult situations, the love of hashem is waiting for you.

IT'S DIFFICULT TO CHANGE. IT'S DIFFICULT TO BE CONSISTENT WITH MITZVAHS, WITH DAVENING, WITH MEDITATION. THAT ONLY PROVES HOW IMPORTANT THEY ARE.

EVERY DAY IS A TOTALLY NEW CREATION. NO TWO DAYS ARE EVER THE SAME. EVERY DAY IS A LIFE FOR ITSELF. EVERY DAY HASHEM SENDS MESSAGES HOW TO GET CLOSE TO HIM. BUT OFTEN THESE MESSAGES PASS US BY.

Meditate half an hour every day. TALK TO HASHEM. MAKE IT A REALITY. THE MESSAGES WILL BECOME MORE CLEAR. Bug Him. Thank Him.

5.29

ב Kislev 5758

# ❧ SOUL ADVENTURE #11 ❧

## REFLECTION:

How can you bring G-d into your life today?

## ❧ YOUR NOTES, INSIGHTS, & DOODLES ❧

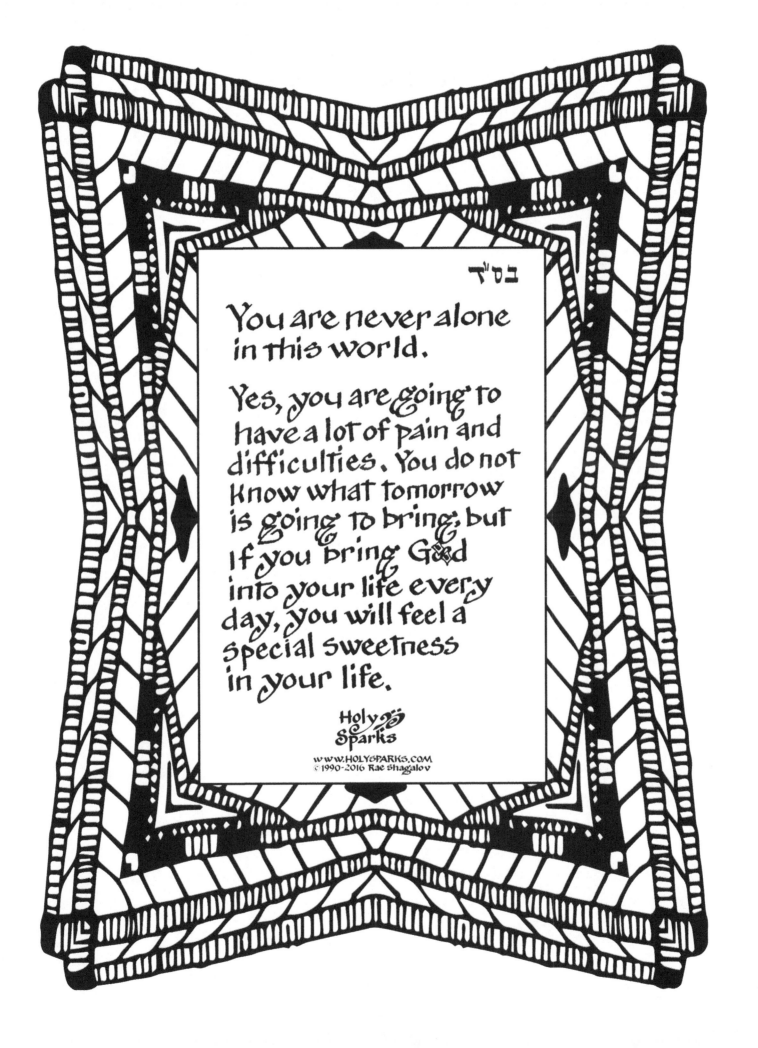

בס"ד

You are never alone
in this world.

Yes, you are going to
have a lot of pain and
difficulties. You do not
know what tomorrow
is going to bring, but
if you bring G‑d
into your life every
day, you will feel a
special sweetness
in your life.

Holy
Sparks

# YOUR NOTES, INSIGHTS, & DOODLES

# YOUR NOTES, INSIGHTS, & DOODLES

In each of us there is an inner unpeacefulness. ב"ה

# שלום

## Peace is the strength To say, "I forgive you."

IT'S UP TO YOU! TODAY CAN BE KVETCHY OR IT CAN BE GREAT.

"THIS IS MY DAY AND I'M GOING TO ENJOY IT!"

IF THINGS GO BADLY SOMEWHERE ELSE, DON'T TAKE IT OUT ON YOUR LOVED ONES!

# Misplaced Anger?

## It's much easier To be critical than complimentary

BY EXPRESSING HIS LOVE FOR HASHEM ZEALOUSLY, PINCHAS DREW OFF THE DIVINE ANGER TO THE BAIS HAMIKDASH. INSTEAD OF DESTROYING THE JEWISH PEOPLE FOR THEIR SINS, G·O·D DESTROYED HIS OWN HOUSE. FOR THIS, PINCHAS WAS GIVEN THE GIFT OF LIVING FOREVER. HE BECAME ELIAHU HANAVI, THE ONE WHO STRENGTHENS THE JEWISH PEOPLE TO KEEP LEARNING TORAH.

# עז
## Inner Strength

## Only Together can a man and a woman achieve peace.

EVERY PERSON HAS A PART INSIDE THAT DOESN'T WANT TO LIVE, THAT DOESN'T WANT TO GET UP TO MEET THE DAY, THAT DOESN'T WANT TO ENJOY THE DAY.

## Smile.

THE WAY TO SHRINK THAT ANGRY, KVETCHY PART IS TO TALK TO G·O·D EVERY DAY. KVETCH TO G·O·D ~ NOT TO PEOPLE!

# Blessing only comes with Shalom, with Peace.

## When the Jewish people learn Torah, they are strong. When the Jewish people don't learn Torah, they lose everything.

WE WORRY ABOUT THINGS WE DON'T NEED!

## Get the kvetch out!
WE DON'T HAVE ROOM INSIDE FOR G·O·D WHEN WE'RE FILLED WITH ANGER AND FRUSTRATION AND SADNESS. TURN YOUR KVETCH INTO SIMCHA!

## Empty your mind!
TALK OUT YOUR KVETCH TO G·O·D AND ENJOY THE REST OF YOUR DAY! AFTER THE KVETCH, THEN YOU CAN THANK HASHEM. 20 MINUTES TO A PEACEFUL LIFE!

Holy Sparks
WWW.HOLYSPARKS.COM
©1990-2016 Rae Shagalov

Breslov Shul   PARSHAS PINCHAS   THE 3 WEEKS  21 TAMMUZ
16.17   5762

# ✎ YOUR NOTES, INSIGHTS, & DOODLES ✎

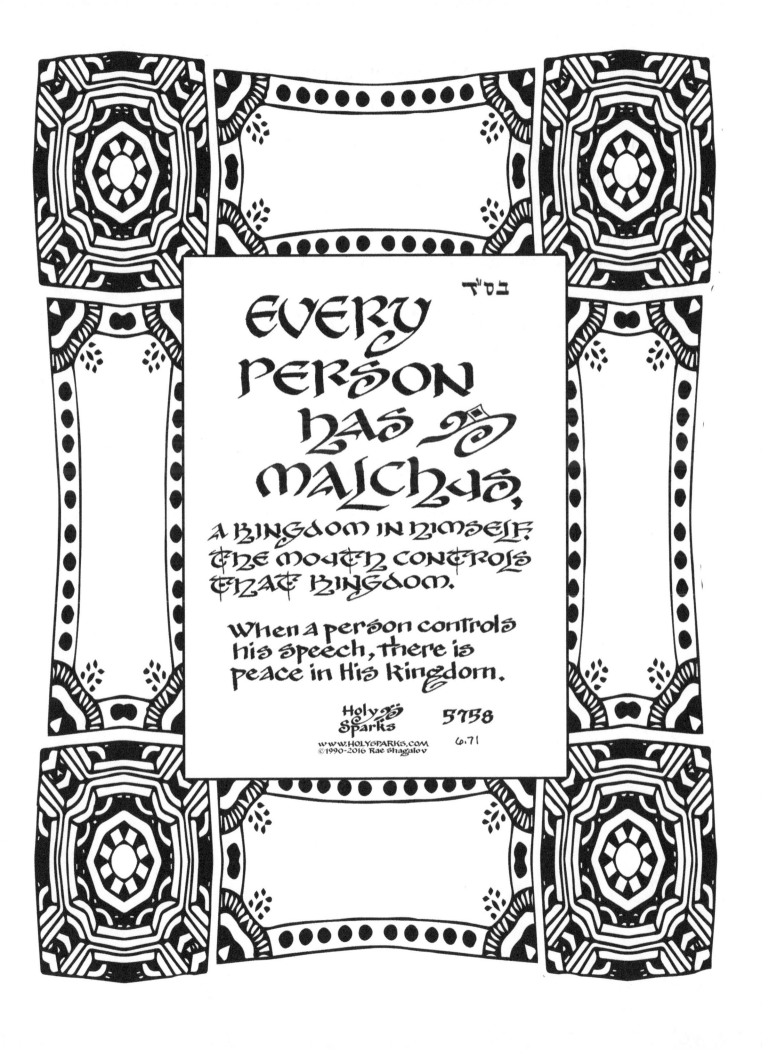

בס"ד

# EVERY PERSON HAS A MALCHUS,

A KINGDOM IN HIMSELF. THE MOUTH CONTROLS THAT KINGDOM.

When a person controls his speech, there is peace in His kingdom.

Holy Sparks

5758

www.HOLYSPARKS.COM
©1990-2016 Rae Shagalov

6.71

# ❧ SOUL ADVENTURE #12 ❧
## MEDITATION

MEDITATE:  In your meditation today, ask G-d, "What can I do for You today?"

SIT QUIETLY and listen to the whispers of your soul.
Keep asking the question until the answer comes.

WRITE: If the answer doesn't seem to come, write or doodle some things that you think G-d would say. It might be something that's hard for you or it might be something especially joyous.

# ❧ YOUR NOTES, INSIGHTS, & DOODLES ❧

בס״ד

Peace begins in yourself. Inner peace comes from learning Torah and creating a strong relationship with G‑d.

THE GREAT TZADDIKIM WERE MASTERS OF PEACE. WHEN WE LEARN THEIR TEACHINGS, WE ALSO LEARN HOW TO BE MASTERS OF PEACE.

NO MATTER HOW DOWN YOU FEEL, NO MATTER HOW DARK YOUR SITUATION SEEMS, YOU CAN STILL FIND THE LIGHT OF G‑D IN YOUR LIFE.

The point of life is to have a relationship with G‑d.

When was the last time you said, "G‑d, what can I do for You, Today?"

By looking for G‑d in your life, by recognizing the G‑dly sparks in everything that happens, that's how you create a relationship with G‑d. Talk To G‑d this is how you make G‑d more real in your life.

Holy Sparks
www.HOLYSPARKS.COM
©1990-2016 Rae Shagalov

22.84

# ❧ SOUL ADVENTURE #13 ❧

## REFLECTION

Is there something that is blocking your happiness?
Are you blaming it on someone or on a circumstance in your life?
How could you take more responsiility for your own inner peace and happiness?

# ❧ YOUR NOTES, INSIGHTS, & DOODLES ❧

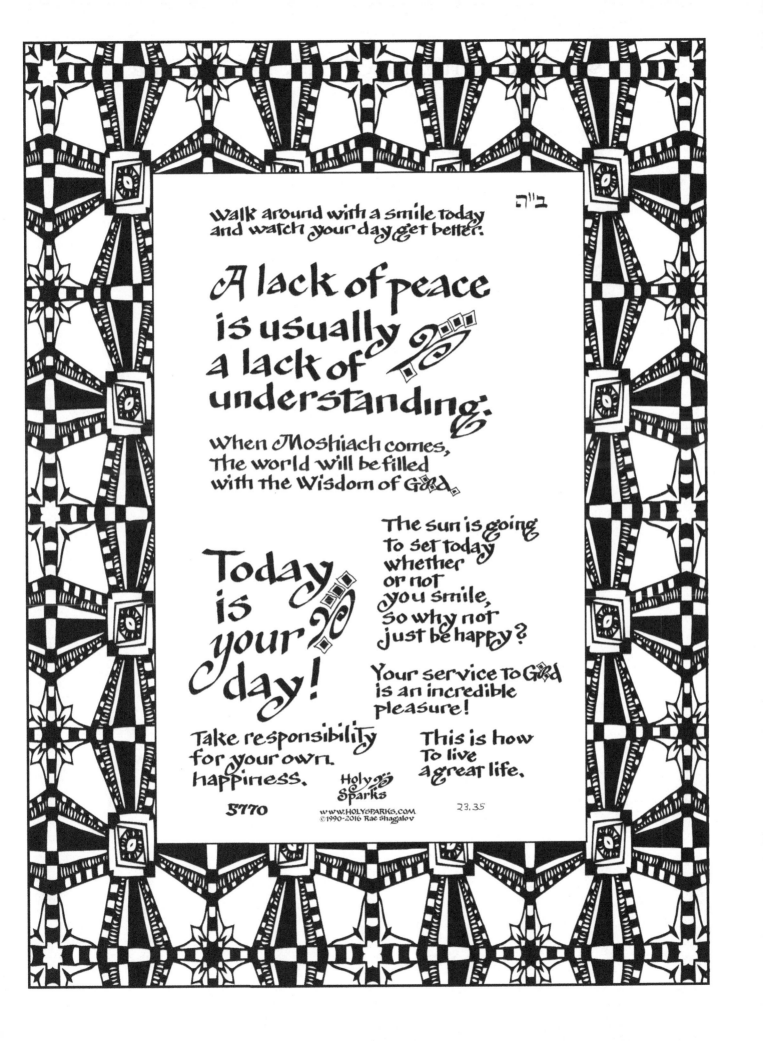

ב"ה

Walk around with a smile today
and watch your day get better.

A lack of peace
is usually
a lack of
understanding.

When Moshiach comes,
the world will be filled
with the Wisdom of G‑d.

Today
is
your
day!

The sun is going
to set today
whether
or not
you smile,
so why not
just be happy?

Your service to G‑d
is an incredible
pleasure!

Take responsibility
for your own
happiness.

This is how
to live
a great life.

Holy
Sparks

5770

WWW.HOLYSPARKS.COM
©1990-2016 Rae Shagalov

23.35

Refresh yourself with Torah today—

בס"ד

BRING TORAH INTO YOURSELF AND YOU WILL BRING PEACE INTO YOURSELF.

FILL YOURSELF WITH TORAH KNOWLEDGE AND YOU WILL FILL YOURSELF WITH LIGHT.

מִי הָאִישׁ הֶחָפֵץ חַיִּים

MAKE G☼D PART OF YOUR LIFE ∞ MAKE G☼D YOUR LOVE. DON'T BE AFRAID TO BOTHER HASHEM.

WHO IS THE PERSON WHO DESIRES LIFE, WHO LOVES DAYS OF SEEING GOOD?

WHY ARE YOU getting up TOMORROW?

YOUR PURPOSE EACH DAY IS TO GET CLOSE TO HASHEM.

Find Hashem in yourself.

EVEN WHEN THINGS GO WRONG ∞ HASHEM IS STILL THERE FOR YOU, SO EVEN WHEN THINGS GO WRONG, Thank Hashem.

HASHEM IS ALL OVER AND HE REALLY LIKES YOU. HASHEM LOVES YOU MORE THAN ANYBODY IN THE WORLD LOVES YOU. THE FACT THAT YOU ARE ALIVE TODAY PROVES HOW MUCH HASHEM REALLY LOVES YOU.

HELP ME FIND YOU IN MY MISERY.

M·E·D·I·T·A·T·E: I WANT PEACE IN MY LIFE.

COVENANT OF PEACE

BRIS SHALOM

THERE IS A deep LONELINESS WITHIN ALL OF US.

FIRST COMES PEACE, THEN COMES LOVE.

Holy Sparks

ATTACH YOURSELF TO THE TZADDIK AND YOUR LIFE WILL BE FILLED WITH PEACE.

LOVE COMES WITH KNOWING THE PERSON, UNDERSTANDING THE PERSON, CARING FOR AND ABOUT THE PERSON. THEN THE LOVE COMES.

IT IS THE LONELINESS OF THE SOUL. NO MATTER HOW MANY PEOPLE SURROUND YOU, YOU WILL FEEL THIS DEEP LONELINESS. TALK TO HASHEM AND WATCH THIS LONELINESS DISAPPEAR.

WWW.HOLYSPARKS.COM
©1990-2016 Rae Shagalov

Ahavas Yisroel Shul LIKUTEY MOHARAN

# ∾ SOUL ADVENTURE #14 ∾

## ACTION

CHOOSE one hour today when you will be around people.
SPEAK a kind word to everyone you meet during that hour.
REFLECT: What happened? How did you feel? How did the people react?

## ∾ YOUR NOTES, INSIGHTS, & DOODLES ∾

**WHEN THERE IS UNDERSTANDING THERE WILL BE PEACE.**

ב"ה

WHEN MOSHIACH WILL COME, THE WORLD WILL BE FILLED WITH **wisdom** AND THROUGH THIS WILL COME PEACE.

FOR ONE HOUR TODAY, SAY A KIND WORD TO EVERYONE YOU MEET.

**TO INCREASE YOUR UNDERSTANDING DAVEN TO HASHEM. WHEN YOU TALK TO HASHEM, YOU FILL YOUR MIND WITH THOUGHTS OF G-D AND YOUR WISDOM WILL INCREASE. STRENGTHEN YOUR HEART.**

*Holy*  *Sparks*

WWW.HOLYSPARKS.COM
©1990-2016 Rae Shagalov

61.59

# ❧ SOUL ADVENTURE #15 ❧

## REFLECTION

CHOOSE something that happened to you that was unpleasant.
SEARCH for the sparks of Holiness in that situation.
REFLECT:  What was one good thing that was in that situation or that
came out of it?

## ❧ YOUR NOTES, INSIGHTS, & DOODLES ❧

On a bad day, See what goodness you can find.

EVEN THE WORST DAYS ARE FILLED WITH GOOD! EVEN IN THE MOST DIRE OF SITUATIONS, WE CAN SING THE GOOD POINTS AS KING DAVID DID. DAVID HAMELECH WAS RUNNING FOR HIS LIFE FROM HIS SON AND STILL HE PULLED OUT HIS HARP AND SANG TO HASHEM.

SING TO HASHEM, SCREAM TO HASHEM, NUDGE, BEG, AND KVETCH TO HASHEM. COUNT YOUR BLESSINGS AND NEVER GIVE UP. M·E·D·I·T·A·T·E 20 MINUTES A DAY. IF YOU WANT TO BE GOOD TO YOURSELF MEDITATE 30 MINUTES.

From Every pain we suffer good comes out.

בס"ד

In the bleakest moment, there is what to sing about.

WE JEWISH PEOPLE ARE VERY STUBBORN. THE FACT THAT WE STILL EXIST SHOWS HOW STUBBORN WE ARE.

USE THAT STUBBORNESS TO STICK TO YOUR MEDITATION.

שלום

How do you BRING PEACE INTO YOUR LIFE?

MEDITATE EVERY DAY AND YOUR LIFE WILL BECOME SWEET.

Learn TORAH

ATTACH YOURSELF TO THE TZADDIK.

ATTACH YOURSELF TO HASHEM.

HASHEM TRULY loves you!

HOW DO YOU KNOW? BECAUSE YOU EXIST. EVERY SECOND HASHEM IS CREATING YOU ANEW. NEVER DOUBT THIS.

EVEN IN THE MOST HORRENDOUS SITUATION,

IN EVERY PERSON & EVERY SITUATION WITHOUT EXCEPTION THERE ARE SPARKS OF HOLINESS.

If you love life and you love yourself, you will be a peaceful person.

IF YOU COUNT YOUR BLESSINGS EVERY DAY, YOU WILL SMILE EVERY DAY.

Holy Sparks

WWW.HOLYSPARKS.COM
©1990-2016 Rae Shagalov

THERE IS A PART IN ALL OF US THAT DOES NOT DESIRE TO LIVE. WE HAVE TROUBLE FACING OUR FAILURES & MISTAKES. WHEN WE TELL HASHEM OUR FAILURES AND ASK FOR FORGIVENESS, EVEN THAT PART WANTS TO LIVE.

5.26

# ❧ SOUL ADVENTURE #16 ❧

CHOOSE: What is one thing you feel like giving up on?
 ACTION: What is one tiny little thing you could do instead of giving up?
COMMIT: When could you do this?
REFLECT: How did you feel after you did it and what was the result?


# ❧ YOUR NOTES, INSIGHTS, & DOODLES ❧

ב"ה

IN EVERY ONE OF US
THERE IS A PART OF US
THAT WANTS TO GIVE UP.

As long as
your heart
is beating
within you,

DON'T
GIVE
UP!

Holy Sparks

WWW.HOLYSPARKS.COM
©1990-2016 Rae Shagalov

# YOUR NOTES, INSIGHTS, & DOODLES

# YOUR NOTES, INSIGHTS, & DOODLES

בס"ד

Live
your
Love
to God

Yes!
God
really
loves
YOU!

Holy
Sparks

WITH ALL
OF YOUR
FLAWS

WWW.HOLYSPARKS.COM
©1990-2016 Rae Shagalov

# ❧ SOUL ADVENTURE #17 ❧

## MEDITATION:

Imagine and experience G-d's immense, unconditional love for you.
Surround yourself with that love.
Fill yourself with G-d's love for you.

## ❧ YOUR NOTES, INSIGHTS, & DOODLES ❧

# I AM TO MY LOVE AND MY LOVE IS TO ME.

## BE STUBBORN.
THE JEWISH NATION NEVER GIVES UP. WE DAVEN TO HASHEM FOR DAYS, FOR YEARS, FOR THOUSANDS OF YEARS ∞ WE NEVER GIVE UP.

IF YOU MEDITATE AND TRY TO COME CLOSE TO HASHEM, THE DEEP INNER INADEQUACY YOU FEEL ∞ DISAPPEARS.

BEHIND THE DOOR HASHEM IS WAITING FOR US TO KNOCK ∞ WAITING TO SHOUT:

## I'VE BEEN WAITING FOR YOU ALL THESE YEARS. WHERE HAVE YOU BEEN?

1 ELUL 5757

I AM TO HASHEM AND HASHEM IS TO ME.

Holy Sparks

# ❧ SOUL ADVENTURE #18 ❧

## MEDITATION:

Listen to your heart.
What is your soul trying to tell you?

## ❧ YOUR NOTES, INSIGHTS, & DOODLES ❧

# THE MOST COMPLICATED THING IN THE WORLD IS LOVE.

We all want to give love, and we all want to receive love. YOU CAN'T FAKE LOVE. IT HAS TO COME FROM THE HEART. MONEY THAT IS GIVEN FROM THE HEART TO CHARITY HAS A GREAT SPIRITUAL POWER. True love is to respect one another for who they are. we say

THERE IS A GREAT POWER IN A COMMUNITY WHERE EVERYONE LOVES AND RESPECTS EACH OTHER. We can learn from everyone. IN EACH PERSON'S CRAZINESS LIES A DEEP WISDOM.

WE WERE COMMANDED TO BRING 13 THINGS TO THE MISHKAN. 13 IS THE GEMATRIA OF

אהבה LOVE
כסף SILVER & DESIRE

THE FOUNDATION OF EVERYTHING IS DESIRE. EVERYONE, POOR OR RICH, WAS REQUIRED TO BRING A HALF SHEKEL. THIS IS THE INNER DESIRE FROM WHICH EVERYTHING CAN BE ACCOMPLISHED.

THE SILVER WAS USED TO MAKE THE HOOKS IN THE MISHKAN. DESIRE IS THE HOOK AND THE SOCKETS WHICH HELD UP THE WALLS.

THE POWER OF 13 IS LOVE.

Your heart is your soul speaking to you. LISTEN TO YOUR HEART CAREFULLY. How? MEDITATE.

The Mishkan united Klal Yisroel. EVERYONE RESPECTED THE KOHEN GADOL. NOWADAYS, WE DO NOT EVEN KNOW WHAT WE ARE MISSING. WHEN KLAL YISROEL HAD THE SHECHINA WITH THEM IN THE MISHKAN, THEY FELT THE LOVE OF G·O·D NEAR THEM.

Desire & long for what you want to be. SAY IT OUT LOUD & YOU WILL CONNECT TO IT.

Parshas Terumah

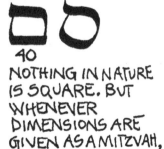

40

NOTHING IN NATURE IS SQUARE. BUT WHENEVER DIMENSIONS ARE GIVEN AS A MITZVAH, THEY ARE SQUARE.

Holy Sparks

# ❧ SOUL ADVENTURE #19 ❧

LIST: Make a list of those who are closest to you. These are often the people who do the most for us by helping us with the small details of our lives, yet we may overlook the value of what they do for us.

REFLECT: Next to each name, write or draw one small token of appreciation you could give or do for them.

COMMIT: Put a date next to each by which you can complete these.

# ❧ YOUR NOTES, INSIGHTS, & DOODLES ❧

# SOUL ADVENTURE #20

## ACTION:
What acts of kindness could you do today?

# YOUR NOTES, INSIGHTS, & DOODLES

# EVERY PERSON HAS A [חן] KINDNESS IN HIS HEART.

This kindness is a gift from Hashem.

Often the pain within us screams so loud we can't hear anything else.

M·E·D·I·T·A·T·E

Talk to Hashem. LISTEN TO HASHEM.

# TRAIN YOURSELF TO LOVE & RESPECT EVERYONE.

## Ahavas Yisroel 5758

# ❧ SOUL ADVENTURE #21 ❧

## MEDITATION

In your meditiation today, surround yourself with G-d's love for you.
Let it envelop you like a warm and loving hug.

# ❧ YOUR NOTES, INSIGHTS, & DOODLES ❧

Look at G-d's record. G-d always comes through! Who is more reliable than G-d?

IT TAKES TIME AND EFFORT TO LEARN TO PUT YOUR TRUST IN G-D.

ב"ה

HOW CAN WE TAKE THE PAIN OF LIFE AND REMEMBER THAT IT IS ALSO GOOD?

How to cope

Like a mother caring for her child... EVEN THE BEST, LOVING MOTHER CAN'T GUARANTEE A HEALING - BUT G-D CAN! THERE IS NOTHING THAT G-D CANNOT DO FOR YOU! EVERYTHING IN YOUR LIFE IS CUSTOM-MADE FOR YOUR SOUL

Remember, G-d really loves you!

Where is G-d? Wherever you let Him in

WE CAN SEE, WE CAN HEAR, WE CAN LAUGH, WE CAN CRY, WE CAN LOVE, AND BE LOVED.

What an incredible gift life is!

WHEN YOU THINK ABOUT HOW MUCH G-D LOVES YOU - IT MAKES YOU HUMBLE.

Focus on what you have, not on what you lack

WHEN YOU FEEL LOVE AND CARED FOR, THE PAIN DOESN'T GO AWAY, BUT STILL, YOU FEEL GOOD.

You are a creation of G-d

G-D LOVES YOU SO MUCH, HE GAVE YOU THE MOST AMAZING MACHINE TO MOVE YOUR SOUL THROUGH THE WORLD. DO YOU KNOW HOW YOUR BODY WAS MADE? DO YOU KNOW HOW YOUR SOUL GOT INTO YOUR BODY? YOU WERE CREATED WITH SO MUCH LOVE AND WISDOM!

Know that G-d is right there with you, holding your hand, in the good and in the bad.

FOCUS ON HOW TRULY LUCKY YOU ARE!

Who knows us best? Who knows what is best for you?

WHO CAN TELL YOU WHY YOU ARE GOING THROUGH WHAT YOU ARE GOING THROUGH? No one

Knows you and what you need better than the One who made you.

G-D BUILT YOU AND HE KNOWS WHAT'S BEST FOR YOU~ EVEN YOUR TRIALS AND TRIBULATIONS.

No one can harm you unless G-D thinks it's best for you.

NO ONE CAN DO ANYTHING UNLESS G-D LETS IT HAPPEN. This is your Test.

Bitachon ' Shevat 5762

Holy Sparks
WWW.HOLYSPARKS.COM
©1990-2016 Rae Shagalov

# ❧ SOUL ADVENTURE #22 ❧

## REFLECTION

CHOOSE something or someone that makes you feel angry.
ASK, "What am I not understanding about this person or this situation?"

## ❧ YOUR NOTES, INSIGHTS, & DOODLES ❧

ב"ה

Another person's anger has nothing to do with you.

The Gemarah says if you want to be rich,

## Respect your wife.

Hate is fed with jealousy.

Money descends from the same pure place as the soul. Money descends as a pure and holy flow of spiritual bounty.

ONLY DOWN BELOW DOES MONEY TAKE PHYSICAL FORM. THIS IS WHY THE SOUL CRAVES MONEY @ BECAUSE THE SOUL COMES FROM THE SAME PLACE AS MONEY. INSTEAD OF CRAVING MONEY @ YEARN FOR AND LOVE THE SOURCE OF MONEY.

PEOPLE WHO LOVE THEMSELVES ARE EASY TO LOVE.

How to be lovable:

## Love yourself

Anger deprives.

WHEN MOSHIACH COMES, THERE WILL BE NO MORE ANGER. THERE WILL BE ONLY KINDNESS. WHEN A PERSON FIGHTS HIS ANGER AND BREAKS IT, THE SPIRIT OF MOSHIACH IS DRAWN INTO THIS WORLD.

HAPPY PEOPLE DON'T GET ANGRY, SO WHY NOT JUST BE HAPPY?

## The more you Tell yourself "G‑d really loves me," the more your prayers will be answered And the sweeter life becomes.

Calm yourself down.

ASK YOURSELF, "WHAT AM I NOT UNDERSTANDING HERE?" UNDERSTANDING OVERCOMES ANGER AND BRINGS PEACE.

Break the force of your anger with love.

BE KIND TO THE PERSON WHO ANGERS YOU.

G‑D REALLY LOVES YOU AND REALLY WANTS YOU TO BECOME BETTER.

THE FACT THAT YOUR HEART IS BEATING AND YOU WOKE UP THIS MORNING PROVES THAT G‑D LOVES YOU AND WANTS YOU.

True love comes from understanding and caring for another.

"ADVICE ON ANGER"

EREV TU B'AV
5770

# ❧ SOUL ADVENTURE #23 ❧

## APPRECIATION ADVENTURE

CHOOSE one hour of your day for this Appreciation Adventure.

NOTICE every good thing, small or great, that you appreciate or respect in each person you meet - even strangers you've never seen before.

COMPLIMENT: As much as possible - and even more than what is comfortable - tell each person why you appreciate or respect him or her.

RECORD the results and highlights of your Appreciation Adventure.

REFLECT: What feelings arose for you? How did the people react to your compliments?

SCHEDULE your next Appreciation Hour.

# ❧ YOUR NOTES, INSIGHTS, & DOODLES ❧

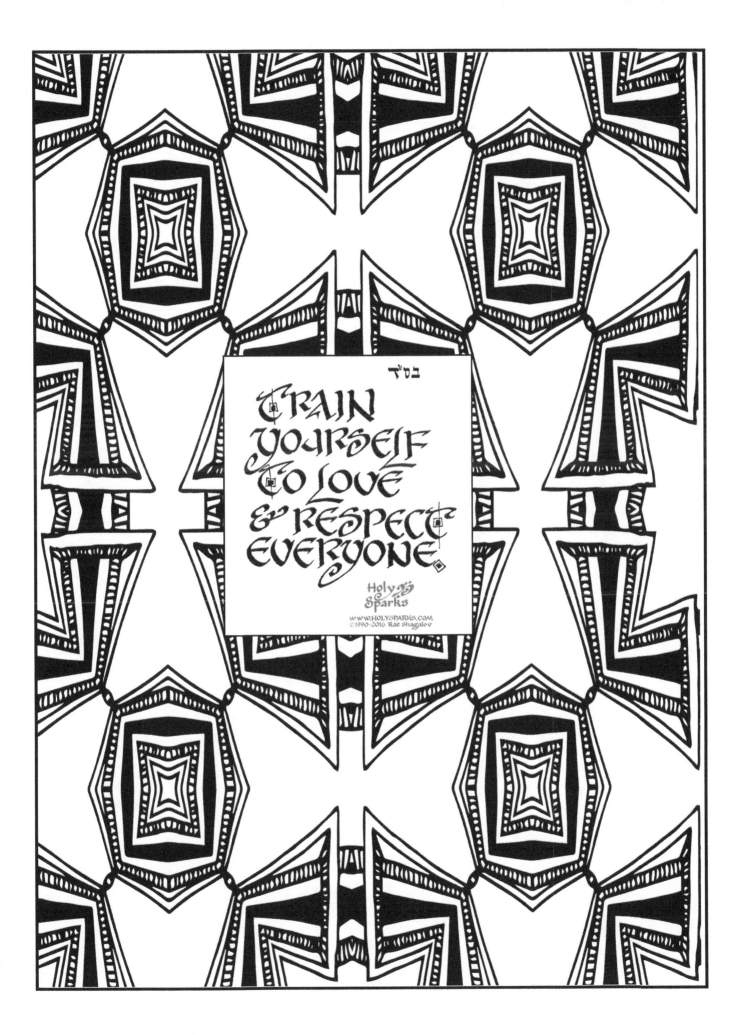

בס״ד

TRAIN
YOURSELF
TO LOVE
& RESPECT
EVERYONE.

Holy
Sparks

WWW.HOLYSPARKS.COM
©1990-2016 Rae Shagalov

בס"ד

G‑d is with you ALL the time!

You are wanted by G‑d.

Shower your child with love. CHILDREN NEED TO FEEL LOVED AND WANTED ALWAYS TO BE SUCCESSFUL IN LIFE.

As long as you have ups and downs, you know you are alive.

SOMETIMES YOU GET UP AND FEEL SO EXCITED TO BE ALIVE. OTHER TIMES YOU GET UP AND YOU'RE ANNOYED WITH EVERYONE ⊕ ESPECIALLY YOURSELF.

Everything is bashert.

When love is flowing; everything flows.

THE HAPPIER YOU ARE, THE MORE EVERYTHING FLOWS.

No MATTER HOW DIFFICULT THINGS MIGHT BE, WHEN YOU REMEMBER THAT G‑D LOVES YOU, EVERYTHING IS EASIER.

REMEMBER HOW MUCH YOU LOVE G‑D.

I am to my love and my love is to me.

THE UPS IN LIFE

THE DOWNS IN LIFE

WHEN YOU ARE FEELING DOWN, REMEMBER G‑D LOVES YOU AND WANTS YOU.

WHEN YOU REALLY WANT SOMETHING, YOU'LL MAKE SURE IT GETS DONE.

If you want to do something ⊕ it will get done!

YOU CAN TOLERATE PAIN BETTER. EVERYTHING SEEMS BETTER. YOU GOT UP THIS MORNING, YOUR HEART IS BEATING ⊕ THAT MEANS G‑D LOVES YOU ⊕ THAT MEANS G‑D WANTS YOU! ISN'T IT GOOD TO BE LOVED AND WANTED?

Know your vulnerabilities.

Then you will know how to get up when you are down.

Ratzon Will RUNNING ⊕ WHEN A PERSON REALLY WANTS SOMETHING, HE RUNS TOWARD IT.

Happiness Helps Everything!

Elul is a loving time. G‑d comes to us in the field.

Holy Sparks

5770

www.HOLYSPARKS.COM
©1990-2016 Rae Shagalov

# YOUR NOTES, INSIGHTS, & DOODLES

# ❧ SOUL ADVENTURE #24 ❧

## MEDITATION
*ASK, "What am I doing?"*
REPEAT.

RECORD your answers here in words or images.
REFLECT: Are these the things you want to be doing with your life?
If yes, how can you do them even better or more often?
If not, how can you disgard, discontinue, or change the things that you are doing that are not serving you or others?

# ❧ YOUR NOTES, INSIGHTS, & DOODLES ❧

בס"ד

# Your good points are your greatest wealth.

CONNECT YOUR THOUGHTS TO THE KEDUSHA OF YOUR MITZVAHS.

IF YOU FEEL SPECIAL IN THE EYES OF HASHEM, WHEN YOU FEEL LOVED AND CARED FOR BY HASHEM, IT IS EASY TO DO CHESED AND TO STAY OUT OF TROUBLE.

HOW DO YOU STAY CONNECTED TO HASHEM?

MEDITATE

YOU MUST TRAIN YOURSELF TO DO CHESED BUT

IF YOU ARE ASKED TO DO A CHESED WHICH YOU WILL RESENT DEEPLY, DON'T DO IT BECAUSE THE MITZVAH WILL NOT BE A MITZVAH.

# CHERISH WHAT YOU HAVE, IT'S YOUR LIFE, LIVE IT!

CHESED IS WHEN WE ARE GIVING, LOVING AND KIND-HEARTED.

GEVURAH: WE ALL HAVE A STREAK OF MEANNESS IN US.

A PERSON WHO IS ONLY GEVURAH IS A PIECE OF WOOD THAT DRIES UP. IT DOESN'T PRODUCE ANYTHING. WHEN CHESED RULES OVER GEVURAH, EVERYTHING FALLS INTO PLACE.

## If you want the best of someone to come out...

TREAT HIM NICELY.

NO MATTER HOW DRY THE STICK IS, CHESED CAN MAKE IT BLOOM. THE LOVE AND KINDNESS HAS TO COME FIRST.

YOU MUST TEACH YOURSELF TO DO CHESED.

WE ALL HAVE THE TIME TO MEDITATE AND DO CHESED, BUT THE YETZER HARA GETS IN THE WAY.

## When everything is chaos, common sense is great wisdom.

FIND A FRIEND TO ASK YOU NOW AND THEN:

### What are you doing?

EVERYBODY EXPERIENCES TUMULT AT SOME POINT IN THEIR LIVES. MEDITATE AND ASK YOURSELF:

### What am I doing?

## Mischief needs company.

## RESPECT YOURSELF. BE HAPPY WITH YOURSELF.

STUBBORN PEOPLE OFTEN FEEL THEY ARE NOT BEING RESPECTED.

## RESPECT OTHERS AND YOU'LL HAVE KAVOD FOR YOURSELF. 7.15

Holy Sparks
WWW.HOLYSPARKS.COM
©1990-2016 Rae Shagalov

# June 28, 5758

# ~ SOUL ADVENTURE #25 ~
## DRAW THE GOODNESS OUT

REVIEW: Before going to sleep tonight, think about your day today. First look for all of the good points in your day. What did you accomplish? What went well? What small acts of kindness did you do? What made you happy? What made others happy?

REFLECT: What was hard for you? What would you like to change in how you did things? What would you like to improve?

WRITE the good points in the left column and the things that need improvement in the right column.

PLAN: What would you like to increase or decrease tomorrow? Write them below.

| GOOD POINTS | NEEDS IMPROVEMENT |
|---|---|
| | |
| INCREASE | DECREASE |

Cheshbon Hanefesh Accounting of the Soul

DID YOU ACCOMPLISH WHAT YOU WANTED TO ACCOMPLISH TODAY? WHAT COULD YOU DO DIFFERENTLY TOMORROW?

REVIEW YOUR DAYS OR THE DAYS WILL GO BY AND YOU WILL WONDER WHAT HAPPENED TO THEM.

When you review your deeds at the end of the day, THAT IS A DAY YOU REALLY LIVED.

ב״ה

DON'T LET LIFE GO!

Work to be happy!

A Jewish Soul can never be extinguished. Every Jewish heart has good in it.

CONNECT TO THE GOODNESS OF YOUR SELF.

SOMETIMES A PERSON HAS TO BE CHALLENGED TO BRING THE GOOD OUT.

YAAKOV AVINU LIVED ALL THE DAYS OF HIS LIFE. HE TOOK ALL OF HIS DAYS WITH HIM.

Are you afraid to live life?

THERE IS NO PLACE; THERE IS NO SITUATION IN WHICH YOU CANNOT FIND G‑D.

THE PERSON WHO THINKS ABOUT HIS DEATH IN A HEALTHY WAY REALLY KNOWS HOW TO LIVE, BECAUSE HE KNOWS HIS LIMITS.

When you're happy, you're living. When you're not happy, you're not living.

Everyone has something good in him. The trick is to find those good points and encourage them to come out.

When you have to fight for something, you cherish it.

YOU CAN'T CALL THE TROUBLES OF LIFE BAD. YOU HAVE TO CALL THEM TESTS. YOUR SITUATION IS CUSTOM-MADE TO CHALLENGE YOU TO BRING OUT YOUR GOOD POINTS AND CHERISH YOUR LIFE.

THERE IS NOTHING AS POWERFUL AS A HAPPY DISPOSITION!

Draw the goodness out! Grab hold of the good points and bring them out.

You are not alone! THERE IS NO SUCH THING AS A TROUBLE-FREE LIFE. THE TRICK OF LIFE IS TO CHERISH THE GOOD IN THE MIDST OF THE TROUBLES AND TO REMEMBER THAT G‑D IS WITH YOU ALWAYS. YOU ARE NOT ALONE IN YOUR TROUBLES; G‑D IS WITH YOU THERE.

Trust G‑d.

Holy Sparks

When you are happy, you are full of life.

WHEN YOU GET IN TOUCH WITH THE GOODNESS IN YOURSELF, YOU CAN OVERCOME ANY UNHAPPINESS. CONNECT TO YOUR GOODNESS UNTIL IT RISES TO THE TOP. HOW DO YOU CLIMB OUT OF SADNESS? FOCUS ON THE GOOD!

17.28

# ❧ SOUL ADVENTURE #26 ❧

## GOODNESS MEDITATION

In your meditation today, thank G-d for every little bit of goodness you can find in your day. Celebrate them! Write, doodle and decorate them below.

## ❧ YOUR NOTES, INSIGHTS, & DOODLES ❧

CELEBRATE your Good?

DID YOU MEDITATE TODAY? IF YOU MEDITATE EVERY DAY FOR 40 DAYS, YOU WILL NOTICE MUCH GOOD IN YOUR LIFE.

בס"ד

# ❧ SOUL ADVENTURE #27 ❧
## YOUR RESISTANCE ADVENTURE

CHOOSE one thing that is hard for you to resist.

RESIST! Begin resisting it and continue for 24 hours.

TRY AGAIN - even if you have tried a million times before and failed, that's okay. Try again.

COUNT how many times (or minutes or hours) that you were successfully resisting it. Even if you fail, count it anyway.

TRY AGAIN multiple times throughout the day. Be sure to continue and count how many times you resisted, whether you were successful or not.

CELEBRATE each time you were successful, even if it was only for one micro-second! Every little bit of effort creates a residue of success that attracts more success to it.

PRAISE G-d for your success and praise yourself for your effort, "At least I tried, and I was successful in some small way."

# ❧ YOUR NOTES, INSIGHTS, & DOODLES ❧

בס"ד

# We are so blessed!

we should be walking around Smiling from ear-to-ear.

I'M HAPPY I'M ALIVE. I'M HAPPY I HAVE WHAT I HAVE.

## The more you have Faith, the calmer you feel.

When things don't go well, ask yourself: "What can I change?"

THIS CLEANS OUT ALL OF THE IMPURITIES:
• ANGER • GOSSIP • COMPLAINING •

# Is it worth it?

When you are happy everything goes better.

EVERYTHING THAT HAPPENS TO YOU IS FOR YOUR BENEFIT.

When you do Teshuva out of love, your mind opens to new levels of understanding.

Think of all of the blessings and goodness G-d bestows upon you.

THIS WILL PUT YOU IN THE RIGHT FRAME OF MIND TO DO TESHUVA OUT OF LOVE, TO FEEL SAD THAT YOU HAVE LET DOWN THE MASTER OF THE UNIVERSE.

# Live every day of life fully!

Today is going to be the way you make it.

## Just clean up one little mess in your life.

EVEN IF YOU CAN ONLY HOLD YOURSELF BACK FROM SOMETHING FOR ONE SECOND @ CELEBRATE THAT ONE SECOND OF SUCCESS!

### Faith is built on Truth.

WHATEVER HAPPENS TO YOU @ THERE IS A REASON FOR IT,

# Focus on the good in yourself.

Don't let the yetzer hara convince you you're no good.

Celebrate every little step of success.

Choose one thing to work on a whole year.

BE PROUD OF EVERY LITTLE BIT OF PROGRESS. IF YOU FAIL 3 TIMES OUT OF 4 @ CELEBRATE THAT ONE SUCCESS!

# Accept that you are not perfect.

That's the way G-d made us.

THEN YOU WILL BE MUCH HAPPIER AND YOUR RELATIONSHIPS WILL BE MUCH BETTER.
G-D KNOWS HOW HARD IT IS FOR US TO CHANGE AND APPRECIATES EVERY LITTLE EFFORT THAT WE MAKE.

AND IT COMES FROM THE GREAT LOVE THAT THE HOLY ONE, BLESSED BE HE, HAS FOR YOU. WHEN YOU CAN REALLY LIVE THIS TRUTH, IT IS A TASTE OF THE WORLD-TO-COME.

## Rabbi Elchonon Tauber

BEGUN IN ELUL
FINISHED IN AV 5771

23.96

# ❧ YOUR NOTES, INSIGHTS, & DOODLES ❧

## ❧ SOUL ADVENTURE #28 ❧
### SING YOUR GOOD POINTS

REFLECT: What are your good qualities, both those that come naturally to you and those that you had to work to improve?

SING: Make a song out of your good points and sing it!

CREATE: Make a colorful word collage of your good points below. A word collage is a group of words designed or scattered around the page and decorated colorfully.

בס״ד

Collect your good points
and make out of them
a beautiful song

# ᔓ SOUL ADVENTURE #29 ᔓ
## LONG LIFE MEDITATION

IMAGINE yourself at 120 years old, at the end of your long life and about to depart from this world.

ASK YOURSELF, *"What did I accomplish with my life?"*

REFLECT: Is there anything else you feel you should have accomplished by the end of your life but didn't?

PLAN: How could you begin that now or do it in some small, scaled-down way?

# ᔓ YOUR NOTES, INSIGHTS, & DOODLES ᔓ

בס"ד

# CELEBRATE your Good

**YOU ARE WHAT YOU ARE, NOT MORE AND NOT LESS.**

**I SING TO HASHEM WHAT IS IN ME.**

**COLLECT YOUR GOOD POINTS AND MAKE OUT OF THEM A BEAUTIFUL SONG.**

THERE WAS A MAN, AND EVERYTHING IN HIS LIFE BECAME NO GOOD. HIS WIFE NAGGED HIM, HIS MOTHER INTERFERED, HIS CHILDREN WERE TOO NOISY, HIS BUSINESS WENT SOUR. FINALLY, THE MAN COULD TAKE IT NO MORE. HE WENT TO THE SEA AND BEGGED THE MALACH OF THE SEA TO TAKE HIM. SO HE WENT TO LIVE IN THE SEA. AT FIRST IT WAS SO PEACEFUL, SO BEAUTIFUL, SO FULL OF TRANQUILITY, INCREDIBLE FISHES, GRACEFUL SEAWEEDS, PLENTY OF QUIET. BUT AFTER A FEW WEEKS HE ASKED THE MALACH TO SEND HIM BACK. "WHAT! WHY?" ASKED THE MALACH. "WHAT ABOUT YOUR WIFE? YOUR MOTHER? YOUR CHILDREN? YOUR BUSINESS?" I MISS MY WIFE! I MISS MY MOTHER! I MISS MY CHILDREN! I MISS MY BUSINESS! I MISS THE SUNSETS! I MISS THE..."

HOW DO WE AVOID BEING INFLUENCED BY THE NEGATIVITY OF THIS WORLD? SING TO HASHEM! SING TEHILLIM! PRAY! MEDITATE! CONNECT TO HASHEM WITH YOUR PRAYER.

DID YOU MEDITATE TODAY? IF YOU MEDITATE EVERY DAY FOR 40 DAYS, YOU WILL NOTICE MUCH GOOD IN YOUR LIFE.

A DAY WITHOUT MEDITATION IS LIKE A DIFFERENT DAY. NO ONE IS LATE TO THE MOVIES. NO ONE IS LATE TO HIS OWN PARTY. NO ONE IS LATE TO THE YETZER HARA... BUT WHEN IT IS TIME TO MEDITATE, TO PRAY... WHEN WE ARE GOING TO DO SOMETHING POSITIVE-- THAT IS WHEN RESISTANCE COMES.

WHEN YOU YOU ARE UNHAPPY NOTHING IS GOOD, SO WHY NOT JUST BE HAPPY?!

PICTURE YOURSELF 120 YEARS OLD AND ABOUT TO DEPART THIS LIFE. ASK YOURSELF, "WHAT DID YOU ACCOMPLISH? DID YOU DO WHAT YOU WERE SENT TO THIS WORLD TO DO?" WAKE UP & DO IT!

WE SING TO HASHEM IN OUR DARKNESS, AND HE ANSWERS OUR PRAYERS WITH LIGHT.

DON'T FALL IN LOVE. FIRST LOOK AT WHO THE PERSON IS. THEN FALL IN LOVE.

**where are you holding? What have you accomplished?**

Rabbi Tauber @ R. Citron's Shul July 6, 5757

# ✎ SOUL ADVENTURE #30 ✎
## GIVE YOURSELF A LITTLE PUSH

REFLECT: What is one mitzvah that you would like to begin or improve in your spiritual practice?

PLAN: How could you begin that now? What baby-step or giant-step could you take?

PUSH: Who could help you or what would you need to give you a gentle push in the right direction?

## ✎ YOUR NOTES, INSIGHTS, & DOODLES ✎

ב"ה

G‑d focuses on our goodness, on your goodness.

NONE OF US KNOW WHAT OTHERS GO THROUGH, HOW MUCH PAIN THEY HAVE AND HOW HARD LIFE IS FOR THEM. SO HOW CAN WE JUDGE THEM?

G‑D KNOWS HOW MUCH EFFORT IT TAKES TO DO EVEN THE SMALLEST OF HOLY THINGS AND IS SO PROUD OF EVEN THE TINIEST EFFORTS TO DO GOOD AND THE SMALLEST EFFORTS TO RESIST NOT-GOOD.

Your mind is the Holy of Holies. Keep it pure!

Every detail of the world is the will of G‑d. There is a reason for everything.

The focus of G‑d is on the good things that you do.

You have never lived a day like today.

G‑d is proud of YOU in a million different ways!

"I BELIEVE IN G‑D AND I FOLLOW IN G‑D'S WAYS. NO MATTER HOW HARD IT IS, I KEEP SHABBOS, I KEEP KOSHER, I GIVE MY CHILDREN A JEWISH EDUCATION." THIS MAKES G‑D SO PROUD!

Every small thing you do to push yourself to do the right thing, no matter how small G‑d is so proud of you!

Rabbi Elchonon Tauber   6 Kislev 5770   22.68

Holy Sparks

# ❧ SOUL ADVENTURE #31 ☙

## POSITIVE THOUGHTS MEDITATION

CREATE: Make a list or a colorful word collage below of the positve thoughts you want to focus on for 20 minutes today. (A word collage is a group of words designed or scattered around the page and decorated colorfully.)

## ❧ YOUR NOTES, INSIGHTS, & DOODLES ☙

בס"ד

# Your Soul needs G‑d.

**You are what you think.**
CONTROL YOUR NEGATIVE THOUGHTS
BY TALKING TO G‑D.
BRING OUT YOUR
PASSION AND
CONNECT IT TO
YOUR GOODNESS.

WHEN YOU
THINK ABOUT
THE GOOD IN
YOUR LIFE
AND IN
YOURSELF,
YOU BEGIN
TO SURROUND
YOURSELF
WITH
GOODNESS.

**Push yourself away to make room for G‑d.**
PUSH AWAY YOUR
NEGATIVE THOUGHTS,
YOUR ANGER, YOUR
ENVY, YOUR
SELF-ISHNESS.

YOU CAN
REDIRECT
YOUR THOUGHTS!

**The more you connect to G‑d, the more good is revealed in your life.**

when you think of G‑d, you push away everything negative.

**For 20 minutes today, think only positive thoughts.**

**Train your mind to focus on Holiness.**
TALK TO A FRIEND. TALK TO G‑D.
HOLY THOUGHTS MAKE YOU HOLIER.
THINK ABOUT GOOD THINGS, KINDNESS
YOU CAN DO, WAYS
YOU CAN DO NICE
THINGS FOR G‑D.

DON'T
COMPARE
YOURSELVES
TO OTHERS,
YOU DON'T
KNOW THE
TRUTH OF
THEIR
SITUATION.
JUST KEEP
BRINGING
OUT THE
GOOD THAT'S
IN YOUR LIFE,
IN YOUR
SITUATION
THAT YOU
ARE IN
RIGHT
NOW.

**Focus your heart on what's positive in yourself, your family and friends.**

WHAT MAKES
A GOOD
RELATIONSHIP?

**Do what you need to do AND share your feelings.**
DO THE MITZVAHS WITH CARE
AND PRAY WITH LOVE.

G‑D CREATED YOU WITH ALL OF YOUR STRENGTHS AND WEAKNESSES IN EXACTLY
THE SITUATION YOU ARE IN RIGHT NOW. WHY? SO THAT YOU WILL USE YOUR STRENGTHS
TO OVERCOME YOUR WEAKNESSES AND SERVE G‑D, NO MATTER WHAT!

כ"ד Teves 5770
YARTZEIT OF THE ALTER REBBE

23.2

Holy Sparks
WWW.HOLYSPARKS.COM
©1990-2016 Rae Shagalov

# ❧ YOUR NOTES, INSIGHTS, & DOODLES ❧

בס"ד

Learn wisdom from everyone and everything.

Find the good in everything.

TALKING BRINGS CLARITY.

Focus on the good things.

HOW TO GET OUT OF A BAD MOOD:
◆ LEARN TORAH.
◆ TALK TO G‑D.

Connect with your inner self.

How? Talk To G‑d.

When you feel far from Holiness, what can you do?

USE YOUR MOUTH.

Talk To G‑d.

Open your mouth and pray.

NOTHING YOU SAY EVER GETS LOST. SPEECH IS VERY POWERFUL.

THE TZADDIK

VAV

CONNECTION

YUD

THE PEOPLE

• WISDOM FLOWS
• WELLSPRING

Chochma IS THE VESSEL OF WISDOM.

Bina BUILDS WISDOM.

Daas HOLDING ON TO WISDOM

Everyone has some special goodness with which To serve G‑d.

Then listen To the silence, AND WATCH FOR G‑D'S ANSWERS IN THE GOOD IN YOUR LIFE.

LOOK INSIDE FOR YOUR STRENGTHS.

Everyone has good days and not-so-good days.

How can we make the not-so-good days better?

Bring the goodness out.
Bring out your special goodness.

SPEND TIME WITH PEOPLE YOU ADMIRE AND GET INSPIRED TO GO HIGHER BY THEIR SPECIAL STRENGTHS.

Holy Sparks

Teves 5770

WWW.HOLYSPARKS.COM
©1990-2016 Rae Shagalov

22.89

# COMPLIMENT AT LEAST AS OFTEN AS YOU CRITICIZE

**PEOPLE DON'T REALLY LISTEN WHEN YOU KVETCH, BUT HASHEM REALLY LISTENS IF WE ONLY REMEMBER TO TALK TO HASHEM.**

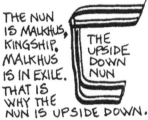

THE NUN IS MALKHUS, KINGSHIP. MALKHUS IS IN EXILE. THAT IS WHY THE NUN IS UPSIDE DOWN.

THE UPSIDE DOWN NUN

# THE KVETCH KICKS IN.

**THERE IS NO VOID IN NATURE OR SPIRITUALITY. IF WE DON'T FILL LIFE WITH HOLINESS, THEN IMPURITY SETS IN. THE YETZER HARA MAKES TUMAH LOOK SWEET, JUICY & DESIRABLE.**

**Everyone gets up in the morning, each with his or her kvetch.**

IF YOU REALLY WANT TO FOCUS ON NEGATIVITY, YOU WILL FIND WHAT TO KVETCH ABOUT.

## RIGHT NOW IT CAN BE GOOD.

THE GOOD OLD DAYS ARE NOW!

## BEWARE OF THE COLLECTIVE KVETCH

DON'T BUY INTO IT! KVETCHING IS CONTAGIOUS, BUT SO IS HAPPINESS.

# PUT THE SPOTLIGHT ON THE GOOD THINGS.

RETRAIN YOUR MIND TO FOCUS ON THE GOOD IN YOUR LIFE.

**when the Kedusha is elevated, the negativity falls away.**

WHEN YOU STRENGTHEN YOUR FAITH AND TRUST IN HASHEM, THE POWERS OF NEGATIVITY FALL AWAY.

THIS SPIRITUAL POWER CAN BE USED IN GOOD TIMES AND BAD TIMES.

YOU ONLY GET ANGRY WHEN BAD THINGS HAPPEN, WHEN YOU FORGET THAT EVERYTHING IS BASHERT.

WHEN CONFRONTED BY KVETCHY PEOPLE, **SMILE,** KEEP SMILING UNTIL YOUR SIMCHA OVERPOWERS THE KVETCH.

**5758** 7.9

Holy Sparks

# YOUR NOTES, INSIGHTS, & DOODLES

LOOK AT THE ULTIMATE GOOD, AND EVERYTHING IS EASIER TO TOLERATE. ב"ה

# The end is going to be good, GUARANTEED!

Look ahead, but stay in the NOW.

You can't run away from pain. You can't run away from a toothache, a headache, financial problems... but you can change how you look at it. Refocus and say, "This is a blessing."

## Chassidus helps you cope.

## A clear mind brings peace.

WHEN YOU THINK: "EVERYTHING WILL BE GOOD,"

# A residue of light remains.

THIS LIGHT IS G‑D'S GOODNESS.

TAKE A VACATION FROM YOUR PROBLEMS ONCE EVERY WEEK.

## Shabbos gives you a clear mind.

TAKE A WHOLE DAY OFF ON THE SABBATH FROM THINKING ABOUT YOUR PROBLEMS, AND INSTEAD, FOCUS ON THE ULTIMATE GOOD YOU WANT IN YOUR LIFE. THIS WILL GIVE YOU A CLEAR MIND TO MOVE THROUGH YOUR CHALLENGES.

## Prayer makes G‑d a reality in your life.

THAT'S WHY THE YETZER HARA WORKS SO HARD TO STOP YOU FROM PRAYING WITH KAVANAH, CONCENTRATION.

## Praying is the hardest thing To do!

IT'S SO HARD TO STAY FOCUSED, TO HAVE KAVANNAH, CONCENTRATION.

### Talk to G‑d.

WHEN YOU HAVE A HARD TIME WITH YOUR PRAYERS, JUST SAY: HASHEM, I DON'T EVEN KNOW WHAT TO SAY TO YOU, HELP ME TO COME CLOSER TO YOU!

# Life is always a change and a challenge.

The question is: How do you deal with your challenges?

REMEMBER THAT UNDERNEATH THE CHALLENGE IS A GREAT LIGHT OF G‑D'S ULTIMATE GOODNESS WAITING TO BE RELEASED

## The ultimate is very good   23.7

# Every Prayer creates a special light and connects you to G‑d in a particular way.

SAY PSALMS LIKE KING DAVID SAID THEM!

Holy Sparks   5770

WWW.HOLYSPARKS.COM
©1990-2016 Rae Shagalov

Happiness

# ❧ SOUL ADVENTURE #32 ❧

## FOCUS ON WHAT'S WORKING

LIST: What's working In your life? What's going smoothly and easily? Make a long list of the details of your life that are going well and that you don't have to struggle with.

## ❧ YOUR NOTES, INSIGHTS, & DOODLES ❧

בס"ד

We live in this world to serve Hashem.
Remember, there is another world.

G‑d is infinite. There is enough for everyone, including you!

WHEN YOU'RE LOCKED UP IN UNHAPPINESS. ACT SILLY

The more loving you are, the more clarity you have about life.

MUSIC CAN ELEVATE YOU OUT OF UNHAPPINESS.

G‑d TAILORED YOUR LIMITATIONS FOR YOUR SOUL.

# Jealousy? Imagination

HAPPINESS IS POWERFUL. YOUR SMILE CREATES A NEW WORLD.

It takes work to be happy.

KEEP FOCUSING ON WHAT'S WORKING IN YOUR LIFE. MAKE A LONG LIST OF ALL OF THE GOOD IN YOUR LIFE.

## Happy people rarely gossip.

PEOPLE WHO SPEAK LASHON HARA, NEGATIVE THINGS ABOUT OTHER PEOPLE, HAVE LOST THEIR FOCUS.

Focus on the good.

THE FACT THAT YOU ARE ALIVE IS THE GREATEST GIFT OF ALL.

LASHON HARA PUSHES THE SPEAKER DOWN, AWAY FROM KEDUSHA, FAR FROM HOLINESS.

Everyone is unique. No one is competing with you.

EVERY PERSON IS DIFFERENT AND HAS DIFFERENT CHALLENGES. OUR IMAGINATION CONVINCES US THAT THE OTHER PERSON HAS A BETTER LIFE, BUT YOU DON'T REALLY KNOW WHAT THEIR CIRCUMSTANCES AND CHALLENGES ARE.

We have to learn to be unselfish and more positive, less critical.

WE HAVE A NEGATIVITY THAT WANTS TO BE EXPRESSED @ IT'S IN OUR KISHKES. DON'T MAKE DECISIONS WHEN YOU'RE FEELING NEGATIVE @ NEGATIVITY CLOGS THE MIND. UNCLOG IT BY DECIDING TO BE HAPPY.

## Born? To Kvetch

The world is not against you.

Life is in your hands.

You can decide to be happy, no matter what. Work on it. SAY: "I WILL BE HAPPY." WALK AROUND THE WHOLE DAY WITH A SMILE ON YOUR FACE @ NO MATTER WHAT! 23,19

Holy Sparks

ROSH CHODESH ADAR 5770

WWW.HOLYSPARKS.COM
© 1990-2016 Rae Shagalov

# ❧ SOUL ADVENTURE #33 ☙

## OWN YOUR LIFE

LIST: G-d sends things to you for a purpose. Make a list of the major choices you've made in your life. Certain things are meant for you. G-d chose them for you and that's why you chose them for yourself.

## ❧ YOUR NOTES, INSIGHTS, & DOODLES ☙

# Develop Self-Happiness.

MATERIAL THINGS WILL NEVER MAKE YOU HAPPY.
THERE IS NO END TO WANTING.

**MEDITATE:**
"I have what G‑d wants me to have. I AM HAPPY WITH WHAT I HAVE."

When we sleep, our souls go to another world, the World of Souls. LEARNING TORAH CONNECTS US TO THIS OTHER WORLD.

If you're happy with what you have, then you have what you have.

DESIRE FOR MATERIAL THINGS IS LIKE DRINKING SALT WATER. THE MORE YOU DRINK, THE THIRSTIER YOU GET.

## This is MINE.

OWN YOUR LIFE. CERTAIN THINGS ARE MEANT FOR YOU. G‑D CHOSE THEM FOR YOU, AND THAT'S WHY YOU CHOOSE THEM FOR YOURSELF.

# Enjoy what you have.

When you are happy with your life, a light shines from you and in you.

## G‑d sends things to you for a purpose.

WHAT IS MEANT FOR YOU WILL BECOME YOURS.

Cherish your home, your family, your circumstances. Look for the good in your life.

G‑D CHOSE THESE FOR YOUR GOOD.

You CHOOSE EXACTLY WHAT'S BEST FOR YOU. THERE ARE CERTAIN HOLY SPARKS IN THE THINGS YOU BUY, WEAR, EAT, USE & THAT ARE MEANT ONLY FOR YOU.

# Born To Kvetch.

WHO IS BORN GRATEFUL? THIS IS OUR WORK. WE HAVE TO DEVELOP OUR APPRECIATION MUSCLES.

## Make an effort but don't force the matter.

IT WILL COME IN THE RIGHT TIME.

# Torah helps us develop inner satisfaction.

LEARNING TORAH FOCUSES US ON WHAT IS TRULY IMPORTANT AND PUTS US IN TOUCH WITH OUR INNER HAPPINESS THAT IS NOT DEPENDENT ON HAVING MATERIAL THINGS.

Holy Sparks

# ❧ YOUR NOTES, INSIGHTS, & DOODLES ❧

# HAPPY PEOPLE ARE SUCCESSFUL PEOPLE.

HASHEM LIKES YOU EVEN MORE THAN YOU LIKE YOURSELF.

NO MATTER HOW MANY THINGS YOU HAVE ON YOUR HEAD, YOU CAN STILL BE FOCUSED. YOU CAN STILL WORK ON INCREASING YOUR KINDNESS, IMPROVING YOUR PATIENCE. YOU CAN STILL MEDITATE.

6.80

# ❧ SOUL ADVENTURE #34 ❧

## "OWN YOUR LIFE" MEDITATION

MEDITATE: "I have what G-d wants me to have. I am happy with what I have."

# ❧ YOUR NOTES, INSIGHTS, & DOODLES ❧

If you appreciate what you have, you have what you have.

IF YOU DON'T APPRECIATE WHAT YOU HAVE, YOU HAVE NOTHING.

THE UPSIDE-DOWN NUN IS MALKHUS THAT NEEDS TO BE ELEVATED, SOVEREIGNTY THAT HAS LOST ITS DISCIPLINE.

**Tomorrow** YOU ARE GOING TO FACE NEW CHALLENGES. THE QUESTION IS: HOW MUCH ARE YOU GOING TO BRING HASHEM INTO YOUR LIFE? WALK THROUGH LIFE WITH **emunah, faith.**

HOW DO YOU DO THIS?

**Pray. Talk to God.** YOU WILL WALK THROUGH YOUR DAY CALM AND HAPPY AND READY TO MEET TODAY'S CHALLENGES.

# To be happy is a BIG Mitzvah!

## But it's not easy to be happy.

WHEN YOU ARE UNHAPPY, YOU WILL FOCUS ON THE ONE SMALL THING THAT ISN'T PERFECT, INSTEAD OF APPRECIATING THE INCREDIBLE BANQUET THAT HAS BEEN LAID OUT FOR YOU.

## The yetzer hara tries to get us to cut corners.

THE YETZER HARA KNOWS IT CAN'T PERSUADE US TO GIVE UP WHAT WE KNOW IS RIGHT ALL AT ONCE, SO THE YETZER HARA SCRATCHES AWAY AT THE EDGES OF OUR HOLINESS.

**Faith** HAS TO BE CULTIVATED EVERY DAY. LAST WEEK'S TESTS ARE OVER.

THIS WEEK HAS ITS OWN AGGRAVATIONS AND BRAND NEW TESTS.

**Every parnassah has its struggle.** THIS IS PART OF OUR ONGOING PRACTICE OF FAITH.

## We lost our two crowns when we started to kvetch.

DID IT HELP YOU TODAY THAT YOU DID NOT SMILE? DID YOU GAIN ANYTHING BY NOT SMILING?

THERE IS A KLIPPAH, A DESTRUCTIVE OR MISLEADING SHELL OF UNHOLINESS THAT TRAPS THE HOLINESS INSIDE OF IT.

## The yetzer hara is waiting beside your bed, waiting to persuade you as soon as you wake up:

THE YETZER HARA GETS UP VERY EARLY!

## "It's not that important."

"DON'T BOTHER GETTING UP YET. IT WON'T MATTER IF YOU ARE LATE FOR DAVENING. STAY IN BED AS LONG AS YOU WANT. WHO CARES?!"

WE WALK AROUND THINKING SOMETHING IS MISSING FROM OUR LIVES. WE ARE WALKING AROUND WITH A HOLE IN OUR SOULS.

SOMETHING IS MISSING FROM OUR LIVES! WHAT IS IT?

**God**

*How to defeat the yetzer hara:* GET UP EARLIER & BEAT THE YETZER HARA AT ITS OWN GAME!

**Holy Sparks**

20 Sivan 5761    13.83

# YOUR NOTES, INSIGHTS, & DOODLES

# ❧ SOUL ADVENTURE #35 ❧

## "MAKE G-D HAPPY" MEDITATION

MEDITATE: "G-d, what can I do for You today? How can I help You? Where in my own life can I do something to make this world a holier place where You can dwell?"

## ❧ YOUR NOTES, INSIGHTS, & DOODLES ❧

בס"ד

# Hashem, what can I do for YOU today?

## How can I help You?!

HOW CAN I HELP THE SHECHINA, G‑D'S INDWELLING PRESENCE IN THIS WORLD, BE ELEVATED?

WHEN THE DALED, THE MALKHUS, THE RESPONSIBILITY, THE THINKING OF OTHERS, IS REMOVED FROM G‑D'S NAME @ ALL THAT'S LEFT IS:

אֲנִי

IT'S ALL ABOUT ME.

WHEN YOU TAKE THE ד OUT OF ANOTHER NAME OF G‑D, YOU ARE LEFT WITH THIS NAME ישע MEANS: SELF

· OUR MASTER ·

# How can you make G‑d happy today?

THE SHECHINA IS IN GOLUS, IN EXILE! HOW CAN YOU, WHERE CAN YOU LIBERATE THE SHECHINA IN YOUR LIFE?

ADAM'S SIN PUSHED AWAY THE SHECHINA. WHAT ACT OF GOODNESS CAN YOU DO TO BRING THE SHECHINA BACK?

## Hishiani
הִשִׁיאַנִי

# It's all about me

IT'S NEVER ABOUT THE OTHER PERSON @ IT'S ALWAYS ABOUT MY FEELINGS, MY NEEDS, MY DESIRES.

HOW TO BECOME LESS SELF-CENTERED.

## What can I do to make my spouse happy today?

The yetzer hara always tries to get us to think more about our selves @ only about ourselves.

## Happiness doesn't come easily @ you have to work at it.

RESPONSIBLE PEOPLE ARE HAPPIER, AND HAPPY PEOPLE ARE USUALLY MORE RESPONSIBLE. WHEN YOU RECOGNIZE SOMETHING IN YOURSELF, IT'S EASIER TO TURN IT AROUND.

## To whom can you give today?

## People who give are happier people.

MAAYON YISROEL · LOS ANGELES · 22.61

Holy Sparks

WWW.HOLYSPARKS.COM
©1990-2016 Rae Shagalov

# ❧ SOUL ADVENTURE #36 ❧

## PICK ONE THING TO CHANGE

CHOOSE one thing you want to change in your life this week to be a happier person.
WRITE your goal for the change you want to make in decorative letters inside the
frame below.
COLOR the frame around it. Tear it out or make a copy and put it up where you will
see it to remind you every day of the good change you want to make in your life.

בס"ד

שמע

**The Crown of Listening**

Gevalt! Never give up! A JEWISH PERSON SHOULD NEVER GIVE UP! NO MATTER WHAT! WE HAVE IT WITHIN OURSELVES TO NEVER GIVE UP.

When the Jewish people received the Torah, THE JEWS SAID, "WE WILL DO AND WE WILL LISTEN." WITH THESE WORDS WE RECEIVED TWO CROWNS. BUT WHEN WE MADE THE GOLDEN CALF, WE LOST THE CROWN OF DOING. BUT WE STILL HAVE THE CROWN OF LISTENING.

When you say Shema in the morning, just remember that G‑d has a plan and you are in it!

When the Yetzer Hara knocks you down, don't give up! Get up and go another round.

THE DIFFERENCE BETWEEN A HUMAN AND AN ANIMAL IS NOT THAT GREAT IF A PERSON DOESN'T ELEVATE HIMSELF.

Our needs are met with wisdom.

Focus a little less on yourself and a little more on G‑d.

Everything runs by the Ribono Shel Olam.

DID YOU MEDITATE TODAY? DID YOU TALK TO HASHEM TODAY? 20 MINUTES IS ALL IT TAKES!

Our day is a different day. What makes it different? The Torah we learn. WHEN WE LEARN TORAH, OUR CROWN OF LISTENING SPARKLES.

Only 6 weeks till your big courtcase. SHOW THE DEFENSE YOU'VE CHANGED ONE THING.

**Work to be Happy**

When you make an effort to be happy, the pain of life is easier to bear.

Pick just one thing to change and work on it all year long. Just one thing!

If you want to be close to your children, respect them! MOST SHALOM BAYIS PROBLEMS COME FROM A LACK OF RESPECT.

ONLY 6 WEEKS TILL ROSH HOSHANNAH — PREPARE YOUR DEFENSE!

16 Menachem Av    14.40    Likutey Moharan 5761

Holy Sparks

# ❧ SOUL ADVENTURE #37 ❧

## SWEETEN YOUR ANGER

CHOOSE one thing that makes you angry.
TRANSFORM:  How can you "sweeten" your anger and transform it with kindness,
love, or gentle words?

## ❧ YOUR NOTES, INSIGHTS, & DOODLES ❧

בס"ד

How can you shed your anger this year?

**Invite the spirit of Moshiach into this world.**
HOW? BY OVERCOMING YOUR ANGER, YOU CAN BRING HOPE TO THE WHOLE WORLD!

**How to calm an angry person down?**

A calming voice calms everyone down.

**If you're not happy, Act like you're happy, and you will be happy.**

**Every person has a mission in this world.**
EVERYONE HAS CERTAIN SPECIAL MITZVAHS TO DO IN THIS LIFETIME. WE COME TO THIS WORLD TO FIX OUR SOULS AND FIX THE WORLD. HOW DO YOU KNOW WHAT IS YOUR MISSION? FOCUS ON THE MITZVAHS THAT PULL YOUR HEART @ THE ONES YOU LOVE TO DO THE MOST AND THE ONES THAT YOUR YETZER HARA BOTHERS YOU ABOUT THE MOST.

Respect your spouse, and love will come to you.

Overcome your anger and rich blessings will come to you.

NEGATED, PUSHED, AWAY UNCARED FOR, IGNORED.

ARE YOU ANGRY BECAUSE THE PERSON DID OR DID NOT DO SOMETHING? OR ARE YOU ANGRY BECAUSE YOUR FEELINGS ARE HURT? ADDRESS THE FEELINGS.

**Sweeten your anger with Kindness**

**Break the force of your anger with love.**
THIS IS HOW TO TASTE THE DELIGHT OF THE WORLD TO COME AND TO SEE HOW EVERYTHING IN THIS WORLD IS PART OF THE MOVEMENT TOWARD THIS ULTIMATE GOAL.

"IT FEELS LIKE I'M THE LAST PERSON ON YOUR LIST." SAY THIS INSTEAD OF GETTING ANGRY.

**Anger puts wisdom to flight.**

Holy Sparks
WWW.HOLYSPARKS.COM
©1990-2016 Rae Shagalov

23.76

WHEN YOU ALLOW YOURSELF TO BE ANGRY, YOU INVITE NEGATIVITY INTO YOURSELF.

# ❧ SOUL ADVENTURE #38 ❧

## WORK TO BE HAPPY

CHOOSE one thing that made you unhappy this week.
REFLECT: What do you think was the message G-d was giving you through that experience?

# ❧ YOUR NOTES, INSIGHTS, & DOODLES ❧

בס"ד

Unhappiness is natural◆ UNHAPPINESS HAS NOTHING TO DO WITH YOUR POSSESSIONS, YOUR HEALTH, YOUR SITUATION.

THE CHALLENGE OF BEING HAPPY IS A VERY POWERFUL CHALLENGE.

YOU HAVE TO CONSCIENTIOUSLY WORK TO ACHIEVE HAPPINESS◆

WHEN YOU ARE HAPPY, YOU ARE ATTACHED TO THE MASTER OF THE UNIVERSE◆

HOW DO YOU WORK ON HAPPINESS? ① LOOK AT THE POSITIVE THINGS OF LIFE. ② ACT AS IF YOU ARE HAPPY AND YOU WILL BE HAPPY! FAKE IT! ③ TALK TO G-D EVERY DAY!

**If you don't work to be happy, you won't be happy.◆**

Today is a day! It's your gift of life! WHAT ARE YOU GOING TO DO WITH IT!?

ARE YOU DOING THE BEST YOU CAN WITH IT?

NO MATTER WHAT IS HAPPENING IN YOUR LIFE, YOU CAN DECIDE TO BE HAPPY!

If you don't make an effort to be happy, you will always FIND something to be unhappy about◆

Our society tells us that if we are unhappy there is something wrong with us. The Truth is that it is our nature to be unhappy.

EVERYTHING IS BETTER WHEN YOU ARE HAPPY!

EVEN THE SHLEMAZEL AT WORK IS NOT SO SHLEMAZELDIK WHEN YOU ARE HAPPY.

**A sigh and a groan are very powerful tools.◆**

Happy people are not so quick to fall ill◆

אור LIGHT

A SMILE IS CONTAGIOUS!

Sometimes you look at a miracle and you don't know what you are seeing◆

IF IT WEREN'T FOR THE ANGEL OF DEATH, WOULD WE EVER DO MITZVAHS?

**Just get up and be happy!**

YOU CAN DECIDE TO BE HAPPY!

WORRY ABOUT WHAT'S UP TO YOU. IF IT'S NOT UP TO YOU, DON'T WORRY ABOUT IT!

**G-d created an empty space with his ultimate wisdom, a space for this universe to exist◆** HE HELD BACK THE POWERFUL LIGHT OF HIS EXISTENCE SO THAT WE COULD EXIST WITHOUT BEING INSTANTLY ANNIHILATED.

**There are things in Torah that are beyond our comprehension.** WHEN SOMEONE HURTS US, THIS IS ALSO BEYOND OUR COMPREHENSION. ANYONE WHO HURTS YOU IS MERELY A MESSENGER. WHEN YOU ARE HURT, DON'T BLAME THE MESSENGER◆ LOOK FOR THE MESSAGE INSTEAD.

WE HAVE A CONCEPT OF GOOD, BUT THAT CONCEPT IS NOT NECESSARILY THE SAME AS THE RIBONO SHEL OLAM'S CONCEPT OF GOOD◆

**The weakness of a person is his greatest strength◆**

◆Rebbe Nachman◆ 5760 LL.71-61

Holy Sparks
WWW.HOLYSPARKS.COM
©1990-2016 Rae Shagalov

# YOUR NOTES, INSIGHTS, & DOODLES

# ❧ SOUL ADVENTURE #39 ❧

## HAPPINESS TRAINING

ASK yourself, "Am I happy?"
REFLECT: What small thing can you do to improve your situation and increase your happiness today?

## ❧ YOUR NOTES, INSIGHTS, & DOODLES ❧

בס״ד

Don't get depressed. Don't ask, "Why?" Ask yourself:

# "NOW WHAT!?"

What small thing can you do to improve your situation and increase your happiness?

When you are not happy?

**Act happy and you will be happy!**

Every morning, ask yourself, "Am I happy?" This is Happiness Training?

**Find good things about yourself and be proud of those things.**

Happiness brings you closer to G‑d.

Find good things in your life and be happy about those things?

**Happiness makes you strong?**

Happiness helps you find G‑d in your heart.

Take the happiness challenge! Put a smile on your face every day this week?

Rabbi Elchonon Tauber

"TRAIN YOURSELF TO BE HAPPY"

2010  23.69

# ❧ SOUL ADVENTURE #40 ❧

## THE 30 DAY SMILE CHALLENGE

Take the 30 Day Smile Challenge. Use the Smile Habit Tracker below to increase the number of times you smile this month. Keep a tally each day of how many times you smiled each day - especially when you didn't feel like smiling! See if you can increase the number of your smiles each day. Watch your happiness soar this month!

 DAILY SMILE HABIT TRACKER

|        | SUN | MON | TUE | WED | THU | FRI | SAT |
|--------|-----|-----|-----|-----|-----|-----|-----|
| WEEK 1 |     |     |     |     |     |     |     |
| WEEK 2 |     |     |     |     |     |     |     |
| WEEK 3 |     |     |     |     |     |     |     |
| WEEK 4 |     |     |     |     |     |     |     |

ב"ה

Don't get nervous.

Don't freeze up.

Take 20 minutes and talk to the Master of the Universe. Just say, "I'm sorry."

Every person has the quality of Malkus, Kingship, the ultimate responsibility.

Appreciation is the glue of friendship, shalom bayis between husband and wife, and our closeness with G‑d.

Happiness has nothing to do with what's happening to you. Why wait? HAPPINESS COMES FROM INSIDE, NOT OUTSIDE. Smile Today!

16.75

Holy Sparks

# ❧ SOUL ADVENTURE #41 ❧

## THE 30 DAY "WAKE UP HAPPY" CHALLENGE

Challenge yourself to wake up happy each day for 30 days.
Color in the daily space for each day that you wake up happy.
Color in the daily space with a different color if you wake up in a different mood,
but change it to a happy outlook within 30 minutes of awakening.

## DAILY "WAKE UP HAPPY" TRACKER

| SUN | MON | TUE | WED | THU | FRI | SAT |
|-----|-----|-----|-----|-----|-----|-----|
| 1 | 2 | 3 | 4 | 5 | 6 | 7 |
| 8 | 9 | 10 | 11 | 12 | 13 | 14 |
| 15 | 16 | 17 | 18 | 19 | 20 | 21 |
| 22 | 23 | 24 | 25 | 26 | 27 | 28 |
| 29 | 30 | | | | | |

## ❧ YOUR NOTES, INSIGHTS, & DOODLES ❧

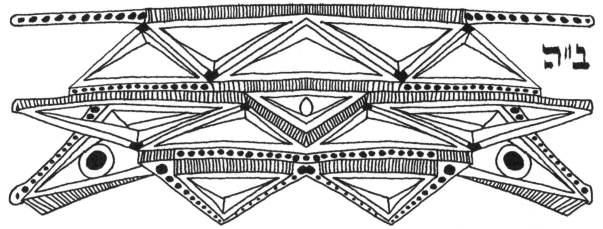

בס"ד

**The way you go to sleep is how you will wake up.**

IF YOU GO TO SLEEP ANGRY, YOU'LL WAKE UP ANGRY. IF YOU GO TO SLEEP WITH HOLY THOUGHTS, YOU'LL WAKE UP IN HOLINESS.

STAYING AWAKE ALL NIGHT AND LEARNING TORAH IS A GOOD WAY TO GAIN FORGIVENESS FROM HASHEM.

# I'm going to wake up happy today.

WHAT YOU ACCEPT UPON YOURSELF IN THE MORNING AFFECTS YOUR WHOLE DAY.

WHEN YOU WAKE UP IN THE MORNING, TAKE UPON YOURSELF CERTAIN THINGS: TO DO A KINDNESS, TO REFRAIN FROM SPEAKING LASHON HARA.

**Yippee! I'm alive!**

SAY THIS WHEN YOU WAKE UP IN THE MORNING, AND YOU WILL SET THE INTENT TO BE MORE ALIVE ALL DAY.

**Davening with Kavanah connects your soul to your self.**

DAVENING WITH KAVANAH IS HARD, BUT IT BRINGS YOU CLOSER TO G‑D.

**Children learn davening by watching adults.**

LET YOUR CHILD CATCH YOU PRAYING ONCE IN A WHILE.

**When you say Shema before you go to sleep, your soul gets refreshed as well as your body. The shema rekindles your faith.**

**Sleep has G‑d's name in it.**

**Sleep 365**

IF YOU OR A CHILD HAS NIGHTMARES, READ STORIES ABOUT THE TZADDIKIM AND BE SURE TO SAY THE WHOLE SHEMA.

2009  18.74

# ❧ SOUL ADVENTURE #42 ❧

## ELEVATE YOUR KVETCH

Set a timer for 10 minutes.
In the left column, make a list of all of your complaints.
In the right column, make a list of every good thing in your life, no matter how small
it might seem. Make your list of blessings longer than your list of kvetches.

| KVETCH | BLESSINGS |
| --- | --- |
| | |

ב"ה

Unhappiness is a perpetual motion machine.

We are blessed to have time to kvetch

Focus on the Good.

Appreciate what you have.

We are so blessed we can even afford to hire people to listen to us kvetch!

Elevate your kvetch!

Do you know how lucky you are to live today?

# ✎ GLOSSARY ✎

| | |
|---|---|
| Adam HaRishon: | The first man |
| Ahavas Yisrael: | Love for a fellow Jew (also the name of Rabbi Citron's synagogue where many of these lectures took place) |
| Aish: | Fire |
| Amalek: | An enemy of the Jews, recurring throughout the generations; the embodiment of evil and doubt |
| Bashert: | Meant to be; sent from G-d |
| Bais/Beis Hamikdash: | The Holy Temple |
| Bina: | Understanding |
| Bris: | Covenant |
| Chochma: | Wisdom |
| Chassid/Chassidic: | Chassidic life and philosophy is a branch of Orthodox Judaism founded in 18th-century Eastern Europe by Rabbi Israel Baal Shem Tov, based on spiritual reawakening through Torah, mysticism and Ahavas Yisrael. |
| Cheshbon HaNefesh: | Introspection; literally, "Accounting of the Soul" |
| Chesed: | The quality of lovingkindness |
| Choson/Chossan: | Bridegroom |
| Daled: | A Hebrew letter with the "d" sound |
| Daas: | Knowledge |
| Daven/Davening: | Pray/Praying |
| Eliahu Hanavi: | Elijah, the Prophet |
| Emunah: | Faith |
| Gemarah: | The collection of Rabbinic writings constituting the basis of religious authority in Torah law |
| Gevurah: | The quality of severity, limitation |
| Golus: | Exile from G-dliness |
| Hakodesh Baruch Hu: | The Blessed Holy One |
| Hashem: | G-d; literally, "The Name" |
| Hitbodedut: | Self-isolation or seclusion; the Jewish meditation practice of speaking privately with G-d |
| Kabbalah: | "tradition," the general term for Jewish mysticism Authentic Jewish mysticism is an integral part of Torah |
| Kavanah: | Intention, concentration |
| Kavod: | Honor and respect |
| Kishkes: | Literally means intestines or guts as in a "gut feeling" |
| Klal Yisrael: | The collective body of the Jewish people |
| Klippah: | An evil shell (so to speak) that obstructs holiness |
| Kodesh, Kedushah: | Holy or holiness; to separate and sanctify what is G-dly from what comes from the opposite of G-dliness or holiness |
| Kohen: | A member of the priestly tribe of the Jewish people |
| Kohen Gadol: | The High Priest who served in the Holy Temple in Jerusalem |
| Kvetch: | To complain |

| | |
|---|---|
| Lashon Hara: | Gossip, evil speech |
| Malach: | An angel |
| Malchus: | The quality of royalty |
| Mishega'ass: | Foolishness |
| Mishkan: | Tabernacle |
| Moshiach: | The Anointed Redeemer, Messiah |
| Mitzvahs or Mitzvot: | Divine commandments (that connect us to G-d) |
| Moshe Rabbeinu: | Moses, our teacher |
| N'aseh v'Nishmah: | To do and to hear; The Jewish people accepted the mitzvahs at Mt. Sinai unconditionally |
| Nun: | A Hebrew letter with the "n" sound |
| Parnassah: | Livelihood |
| Pinchas: | Grandson of Aaron, and son of Elazar, the High Priest |
| Ra: | Evil |
| Ribono Shel Olam: | Master of the Universe |
| Ruach: | Spirit; one of the levels of the soul |
| Shabbos/Shabbat: | The Sabbath day of rest |
| Shalom: | Peace |
| Shalom Bayis: | A peaceful home |
| Shechina: | The Divine Presence as it manifests in this world |
| Shekel: | A coin of Israel |
| Simcha: | Happiness, joy |
| Shlemazel: | An unlucky, hapless person |
| Shmooze: | To chat |
| Teferes/Teferet | The soul's quality of beauty, harmony, balance |
| Tefillah: | Prayer |
| Tehillim/Psalms: | The book of 150 songs and praises of G-d by King David |
| Teshuva: | Repentance; returning to the righteous path of Torah and G-d |
| Torah: | The Five Books of Moses; the entire body of Jewish knowledge; G-d's thought and will condensed in a physical scroll |
| Tumah: | Impurity |
| Tzaddik/Tzadekes: | A pious, saintly man/woman |
| Tzedakah: | Charity |
| Tzimtzum: | In Jewish mysticism, the process whereby G-d concealed Himself in order to create this world with free choice |
| Tzitzit/Tzitzis | A fringed, 4-cornered undergarment worn to fulfill a mitzvah |
| Yartzeit: | Anniversary of a person's death |
| Yehuda: | One of the sons of our patriarch and matriarch, Jacob and Leah |
| Yetzer Hara: | The inclination to do wrong |
| Yetzer Tov: | The inclination to do what is good and right |
| Zohar: | A commentary on the Torah which is a central mystical work of Jewish mysticism |

# ❧ABOUT RABBI TAUBER❧

Rabbi Elchonon Tauber is well versed in a broad range of areas of Jewish scholarship – from the practical to the esoteric – and has attained higher rabbinical ordination in "Dayanus", or Jewish judgeship. In 1984, he was appointed "Dayan" at Congregation Bais Yehuda from where he has been rendering Halachic opinions and decisions for the greater Los Angeles Jewish community. A resident of Hancock Park, Rabbi Tauber is often asked to sit on the rabbinic panels of many of the city's most complex Din Torahs (Jewish court-cases) – most commonly involving questions relating to the societal changes of modern times. While Rabbi Tauber seeks, as much as possible, to confine his sphere authority to the local community, his input and rulings are nonetheless constantly being sought by laymen and community leaders from throughout the world.

Rabbi Tauber's greatest passions, however, remain learning and teaching. He delivers daily "shiurim" (intricate Torah study courses) and lectures throughout Los Angeles in Jewish Mysticism, Talmud and Jewish Law.

# ❧ARTIST'S NOTE❧

Any mistakes contained herein are my own. Although the my Artnotes artistically capture some of the deep insights of Rabbi Tauber's classes, my Artnotes cannot convey the warmth, caring, humor, incredible stories and intellectual challenge you will experience when you hear his classes in person or recorded at:

Breslov.org
http://www.breslov.org/tag/rabbi-elchonon-tauber

And Maayon.com
http://maayonyisroel.com/category/lecturers/rabbi-elchanan-tauber

## ‧ABOUT HOLY SPARKS ‧

Holy Sparks is dedicated to spreading the light of authentic Jewish spirituality and wisdom. Holy Sparks provides and promotes Jewish knowledge, awareness and practice as it applies to people of all faiths and nationalities, regardless of affiliation or background. Holy Sparks helps spiritual seekers, particularly the Jewish people, and others who are looking for inspiration and encouragement, to discover and fulfill their individual talents and potential for serving G-d and mankind through increasing acts of goodness, kindness, and holiness.

## ‧ABOUT RAE SHAGALOV‧

Master calligrapher Rae Shagalov is the author of the Amazon bestseller, *"The Secret Art of Talking to G-d"* and the *"Joyfully Jewish"* series of interactive calligraphy and coloring books for adults and families. Rae is eager to share the beauty and wisdom of Torah through her 3,000 pages of beautifully designed Artnotes that reveal the special message of this exciting time in Jewish History. Rae has combined her experience as a creativity and motivation coach, her talent as a Jewish artist, and her fascinating spiritual search for the true meaning of life to produce these beautiful Jewish Artnotes. Rae's books provide her readers with very practical, joy-based action steps for infusing authentic Jewish spirituality into their daily lives. Rae offers Creative Clarity Coaching for women who want to use their creativity, discover their Life Purpose and elevate their spiritual growth. She is also an innovative educator who develops the talents of children at Emek Hebrew Academy in Los Angeles. Find out more about Rae Shagalov's coaching & workshops at: www.holysparks.com.

## ‧ CONNECT WITH RAE SHAGALOV‧

Sign up to receive free art, coloring pages
and Rae's Soul Tips newsletter!
Go to: www.holysparks.com

LET'S CONNECT!

Facebook.com/soultips

Pinterest.com/holysparks

Twitter.com/holysparks

Youtube.com/holysparksbooks

Instagram.com/holysparks

There's a Holy Spark in each of us
that's hidden very well;
when it's revealed, we make our world
a place where G‑d can dwell.

# ❧ 10 WAYS TO BE JOYFULLY JEWISH ❧

The most important principle in the Torah is the protection of Jewish life. It's more important than Shabbat, more important than holidays or even fasting on Yom Kippur. Right now, in Israel and everywhere, Jews must stand together in unity and do whatever possible to protect Jewish life.

The Lubavitcher Rebbe, Rabbi Menachem M. Schneerson, teaches that there are ten important Mitzvahs* we can do to protect life. We urgently need your help to increase in mitzvahs and merits for the Jewish people. Please choose a mitzvah to begin or improve:

1) AHAVAS YISROEL: Behave with love towards another Jew.
2) LEARN TORAH: Join a Torah class.
3) Make sure that Jewish children get a TORAH-TRUE EDUCATION.
4) Affix kosher MEZUZAS on all doorways of the house.
5) For men and boys over 13: Put on TEFILLIN every weekday.
6) Give CHARITY.
7) Buy JEWISH HOLY BOOKS and study them.
8) Light SHABBAT & YOM TOV CANDLES, a Mitzvah for women and girls.
9) Eat and drink only KOSHER FOOD.
10) Observe the laws of JEWISH FAMILY PURITY.

In addition, the Rebbe urges that:

Every Jewish man, woman and child should have a letter written for them in a Sefer Torah.**

Every person should study either the Rambam's Yad Hachazakah -Code of Jewish Law - or the Rambam's Sefer HaMitzvos.

Concerning Moshiach, the Rebbe stated, "The time for our redemption has arrived!" Everyone should prepare themselves for Moshiach's coming by increasing acts of goodness and kindness and by studying about what the future redemption will be like. May we merit to see the fulfillment of the Rebbe's prophecy, NOW!

---

*Mitzvahs are Divine Commandments that connect us to G-d.

**There are several Torah scrolls being written to unite Jewish people and protect Jewish life. Letters for children can be purchased for only $1 via the Internet at: http://www.kidstorah.org

Listen to inspiring Chassidic Torah classes while you color at:

Maayon.com          Chabad.org          Torahcafe.com

For more information about how to be Joyfully Jewish, visit:

Holysparks.com          Moshiach.net          Chabad.org
Jewishwoman.org        Jewishkids.org        Maayon.com
Meaningfullife.com      Inner.org             Breslov.org

Learn about the 7 special commandments for Righteous Gentiles:
Holysparks.com/pages/7-mitzvahs-for-non-jews

בס"ד

בָּרוּךְ אַתָּה אדנָ-י אֱ-לֹהֵינוּ מֶלֶךְ
הָעוֹלָם אֲשֶׁר קִדְּשָׁנוּ בְּמִצְוֹתָיו
וְצִוָּנוּ לְהַדְלִיק נֵר שֶׁל שַׁבָּת קֹדֶשׁ

TRANSLITERATION:
BARUCH A-TA A-DO-NAY
ELO-HEI-NU ME-LECH HA-O-LAM
A-SHER KI-DI-SHA-NU
BI-MITZ-VO-TAV VI-TZI-VA-NOO
LI-HAD-LEEKNER SHEL SHA-BAT
KO-DESH.

TRANSLATION:
BLESSED ARE YOU, L-RD OUR G-D,
King of the universe, who has
sanctified us with His
commandments, and
commanded us to kindle the
light of the Holy Shabbat.

Lighting Shabbos
candles brings
peace, not only
to the family,
lighting Shabbos
candles illuminates
the whole world.

~ The Zohar ~

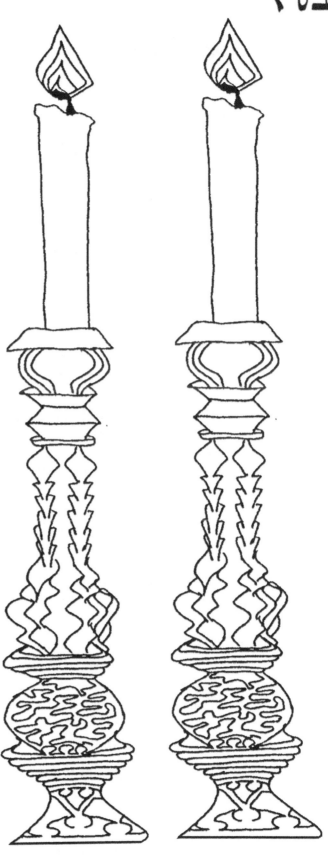

From the Joyfully Jewish Coloring Book.
Available on Amazon
©1990-2016 Rae Shagalov  Sign up for more coloring pages at: www.holysparks.com

# ✸7 SPECIAL MITZVAHS FOR RIGHTEOUS GENTILES✸

*"The word 'commandment' is a translation of the Hebrew word mitzvah, which also means 'connection.' By observing G-d's commandments, a person becomes connected with G-d's infinite will and wisdom and thereby elicits a G-dly light which shines onto his or her soul.*

-Likutei Torah, Rabbi Shneur Zalman of Liadi-

*"The non-Jews have the full length and breadth of Torah—they just have a different role in it. The role of every person is to be a good person, to bring divine light, to draw down G-dliness into the world. To do it as a Jew, as a non-Jew, it doesn't matter. It's the same light, the same Godly energy."*

-Rabbi Yakov Cohen-

There are seven special mitzvahs, known as the Seven Laws of Noah, which are the minimal Torah observance for non-Jews. The Noahide commandments are those that G-d gave to Adam and his descendants and, after the flood, to Noah and his descendants. They are binding upon all of humanity, and were included in the Torah when G-d gave it to the People of Israel at Mount Sinai. Men and women are equal in their responsibility to observe the Seven Universal Laws.

By learning the Torah laws that pertain to all people and performing these mitzvahs (commandments or Torah laws), the righteous people of all nations help perfect this world to a new state of universal holiness, wisdom and peace. "The Seven Noahide Laws" are a sacred inheritance of all the Children of Noah (non-Jews or gentiles), one that every person can use to have a fulfilling spiritual life.

Besides the Seven Universal Laws, the Children of Noah have traditionally taken it upon themselves to fulfill the commandments of honoring mother and father, giving charity, and studying Torah. When a Gentile resolves to fulfill the Seven Universal Laws, his or her soul is elevated. This person becomes one of the "Chasidei Umot Haolam" (Pious Ones of the Nations) and receives a share of the World to Come.

To Find Out More About the Seven Noahide Laws:
www.asknoah.org
www.noahide.org

# ❧ THE SEVEN LAWS OF NOAH ❧

### Believe in One G-d (Prohibition of Idolatry)

Acknowledge that there is only one G-d who is Infinite and Supreme above all things. Do not replace that Supreme Being with finite idols or other gods. This mitzvah includes such acts as prayer, study and meditation.

### Keep the Name of G-d Holy (Prohibition of Blasphemy)

Respect the Creator. As frustrated and angry as you may be, don't blame it on G-d, Who loves you so much He created you and breathes life into you every moment.

### Respect Human Life (Prohibition of Murder)

Human life is holy, as man was created in the image of G-d. Every person is of irreplaceable value. Every human being is an entire world; to save a life is to save that entire world. To destroy a life is to destroy an entire world.

### Respect the Rights and Property of Others (Prohibition of Theft)

Be honest in all your business dealings. Express your trust in G-d as the Provider of life and your livelihood.

### Respect the Family (Prohibition of Illicit Relations)

Respect the institution of marriage. Marriage is a most Divine act. The marriage of a man and a woman is a reflection of the oneness of G-d and His creation. Disloyalty in marriage and other forms of forbidden relationships destroy that oneness.

### Respect All Life (Prohibition of Eating Meat from a Live Animal)

Respect G-d's creatures. At first, Man was forbidden to consume meat. After the Great Flood, he was permitted - but with a warning: Do not cause unnecessary suffering to any creature.

### Establish Courts of Justice

Maintain systems of justice. Justice is G-d's business, but we are given the charge to lay down necessary laws and enforce them whenever we can. When we right the wrongs of society, we are acting as partners in creating the perfection of the world.

# Look for More Interactive Calligraphy Books
## By Rae Shagalov on Amazon

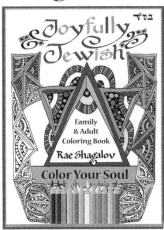

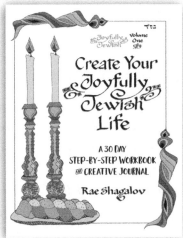

# ❧ CLAIM YOUR FREE BONUS! ❧

Be sure to sign up for your gifts at:

## WWW.JOYFULLYJEWISH.COM/PROJECT/FREEBIES

Not one... Not two... But THREE Free Printable Downloads for you to choose from (you can have all 3 if you like!). Choose the self-care checklist & mini-retreat, the women's mitzvahs creativity pack, or the Jewish Meditation Soul Adventure.

Feel free to share this link with your friends!

# WILL YOU BE KIND ENOUGH TO DO ME A FAVOR?

Have you found anything in this book that was enjoyable or useful to you?
Did you learn anything new or change for the better in any way?
Did anything particularly inspire you or increase your joy?
Or maybe you would just like to say, "Thank You!"

## Please leave a review on Amazon!
Here's the link to find this and all of my other books on Amazon:
http://amzn.to/2ayKVET

It would be very helpful for me and those who are considering whether or not to buy *Joyfully Jewish* books for their own personal growth or to give as a gift to a friend if you would kindly leave a review for this book on Amazon. This will help us reach many more people with this amazing Jewish wisdom that is especially relevant to our generation to prepare the world for Moshiach. Thank you so much!

# ❧ COLOPHON ❧

The Artnotes in this book were all originally handwritten and drawn during classes. The Headings are Felix Titling and the printed text is Tempus Sans ITC. The Dingbats are Windings 2. Some of the coloring pages were digitally modified from the original Artnotes using Repper Pro.

# ❧ CREATIVE WORKSHOPS, ART SHOWS & AUTHOR TOURS ❧
### Are you looking for a truly unique, fun and inspiring event?

- ◇ Book Signing Events
- ◇ Art Shows
- ◇ Inspiring & creative Joyfully Jewish workshops
- ◇ Birthday Farbrengens for you, your group, or someone you want to honor
- ◇ Rosh Chodesh Women's Events

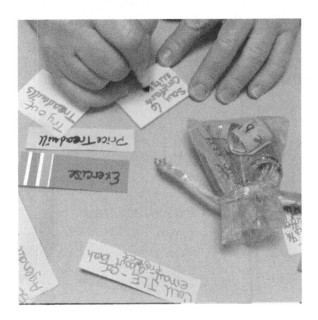

## *"The women loved it!"*
~Mrs. Sara Labkowski, Director, Machon Chana

*"I felt acceptance, warmth, guidance, friendship and sisterhood in the Joyfully Jewish workshop."*

*"Every minute of the workshop was joyful and insightful."*

*"Creating with other Jewish women is awesome. I realized we have so much in common in our journeys."*

## SIGN UP TO GET ON THE MAILING LIST TO FIND OUT ABOUT FUTURE EVENTS AT WWW.HOLYSPARKS.COM

## CONTACT RAE SHAGALOV
## INFO@HOLYSPARKS.COM

## CALLIGRAPHY COMMISIONS, DEDICATIONS, & SPONSORSHIPS

- ◇ Sponsor or dedicate a book or page in honor or memory of someone special.
- ◇ Commission new art, books or videos.

## CREATIVE CLARITY COACHING

- ◇ Work with Rae to clarify your life purpose, create strategies to overcome a challenge, jumpstart your creativity, or plan a new project.
- ◇ Guide your team's creative project with memorable calligraphic recording.

## INTERVIEWS
Would you like to interview Rae or feature her art, videos or articles in your magazine, newspaper, blog, podcast or website?

## PRESS KIT HERE:
## HOLYSPARKS.COM/PAGES/PRESS

The soul is always reaching

Friends and Sponsors

Made in the USA
Middletown, DE
30 July 2023

35957042R00091